The Soybean Industry

The Soybean Industry

With Special Reference to the Competitive Position of the Minnesota Producer and Processor

by

RAY A. GOLDBERG

THE UNIVERSITY OF MINNESOTA PRESS, Minneapolis

LONDON · GEOFFREY CUMBERLEGE · OXFORD UNIVERSITY PRESS

PRINTED AT THE NORTH CENTRAL PUBLISHING COMPANY, ST. PAUL

LIBRARY OF CONGRESS CATALOG CARD NUMBER: 52-12059

Acknowledgments

I AM greatly indebted to Dr. Rex W. Cox, of the Division of Agricultural Economics of the University of Minnesota, whose guidance, constructive suggestions, and continued encouragement have contributed immeasurably to this thesis. I am also indebted to Drs. O. B. Jesness, G. A. Pond, and S. A. Engene for their helpful assistance on various phases of this study.

Dr. Julius Hendel, of Cargill, Incorporated, suggested the general outline of this study and has given constant advice throughout the project. Mr. M. D. McVay, of the Oil Division of Cargill, Incorporated, gave invaluable constructive criticism on all phases of the subject discussed.

Mr. Clive P. Marshall and Mr. Lowell W. Andreas, of Honeymead, Incorporated, kindly granted me complete freedom to examine their processing plant at Mankato, Minnesota, in all its operations.

Mr. R. J. Foote and Mr. Edwin G. Strand, of the Bureau of Agricultural Economics, together with Mr. Gilliland, Mr. Clough, Mr. Jackson, Mr. Jennings, and Mr. Keirstead of the Fats and Oils Division of the Production and Marketing Administration, provided helpful statistical material.

Mr. George L. Levin, professional engineer, provided information that was extremely helpful in analyzing the technical changes of the soybean-processing industry.

R. A. G.

Table of Contents

List of Tables

APPENDIX TABLES

List of Figures

The Soybean Industry

CHAPTER I

Introduction

MINNESOTA, being on the fringe area of the Corn Belt, was one of the last states to develop the soybean crop. Yet today it ranks sixth in total production in the United States. In 1940 Minnesota grew 795,000 bushels, and in 1950, over 16,000,000 bushels (Figs. 1 and 2). The dollar value of this crop advanced from $76,000 in 1940 to approximately $37,000,000 in 1950 (Fig. 3). In the last five years the Minnesota crop and processing capacity have doubled. The problem facing the Minnesota soybean producer and processor is that of ascertaining the probable future trends in the industry that will affect their competitive position.

PURPOSE AND SCOPE

The purpose of this study is to analyze the economic factors affecting the competitive status of the Minnesota producer and processor of soybeans. Such an analysis will provide the basis for delineating the probable future trends in the development of the soybean industry in this state both from the production and processing standpoints. The future of the Minnesota soybean industry is naturally interdependent and interrelated with the national and world supply of and demand for this product. Hence this study will describe and analyze the international and national factors as well as the state factors that affect the competitive position of the Minnesota soybean producer and processor.

The two major hypotheses in this study are:

(1) Minnesota has a comparative advantage in the production of soybeans, and in consequence soybeans can compete effectively with other farm enterprises. If the subsequent analysis confirms this assumption, then one may expect acreage devoted to soybeans not only to be maintained but also to be increased.

(2) The processing industry in Minnesota also possesses a highly

FIGURE 1. Soybean Acreage Harvested for Beans, Minnesota, 1934–1950.

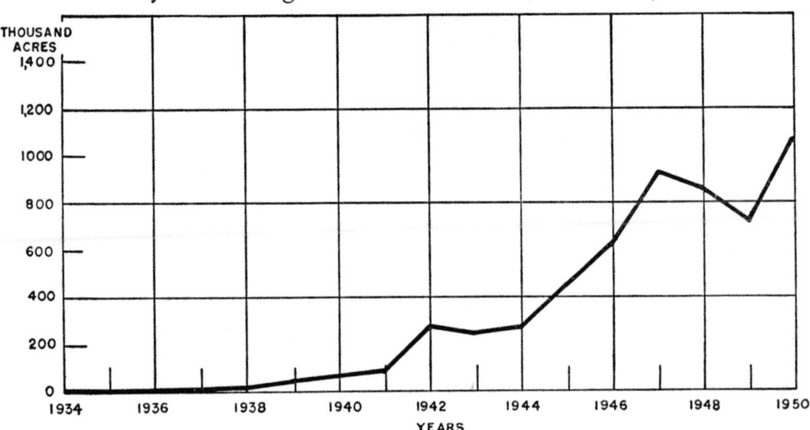

FIGURE 2. Soybean Production, Minnesota, 1934–1950.

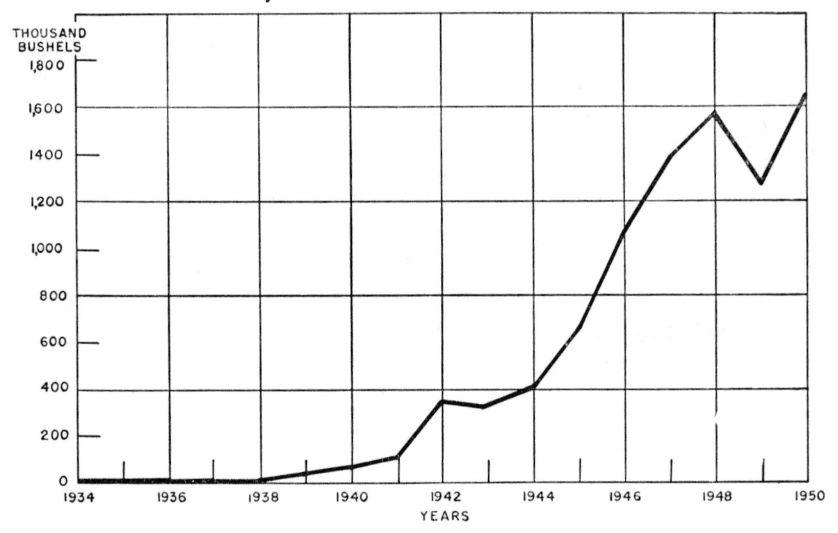

favorable comparative advantage in relation to the processing industries located in the other principal processing states, and in consequence can compete effectively with the latter. Confirmation of this assumption leads one to the conclusion that the Minnesota processing industry will expand provided that soybean supplies remain plentiful and the local demand for meal remains strong.

The first hypothesis is supported by the fact that the income per acre

FIGURE 3. Value of Minnesota Soybean Production, 1935–1950.

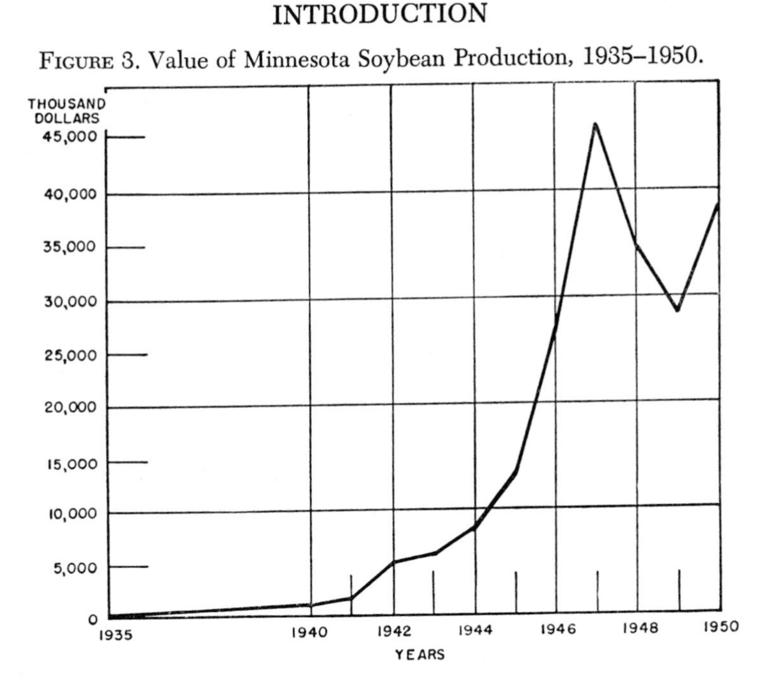

of soybeans in Minnesota exceeds that of any other crop with the exception of corn. One factor that has contributed to this result is the development by the University of Minnesota of new, higher-yielding soybean varieties especially adapted to Minnesota soil and climatic conditions. Another is the excellent markets available for Minnesota soybean production, as evidenced by an expanding state processing industry, the supply requirements of the processing industry in Iowa, and the development of the export market of Canada.

However, there are factors that limit the expansion of the Minnesota soybean crop. The price of soybeans may decrease temporarily if oil prices remain relatively low and the ceiling price of meal is not removed. In addition, the shortage of dollars in the nations of the world that have the greatest potential demand for soybeans and soybean oil will mean fewer exports of soybeans from this country. Also, a settlement of the Far Eastern difficulties will probably result in increased competition from Manchuria in the export market.

The producer's position is interrelated with that of the processor in that the processor provides the major market for Minnesota soybean production; on the other hand, the presence of a Minnesota supply of soybeans gives the processing industry the advantage of short-distance transportation. In addition to a large supply of soybeans, the conditions that support the hypothesis of expansion from the processor's point of view are as follows: the large livestock population in the state and nation that requires additional soybean meal supplies; the increasing transportation rates that enhance the advantage the Minnesota processor has in being able to buy his soybeans freight-off Chicago[1] and to sell his meal on a Decatur, Illinois, plus freight basis;[2] and the fact that the University of Minnesota is developing soybean varieties with greater oil-yield potentialities.

The processor in Minnesota also has to contend with some adverse conditions that decrease his comparative advantage. These include the present low oil content of the Minnesota soybean compared with soybeans produced in Illinois and Iowa; the transportation disadvantage of shipping oil at a Decatur rate to eastern oil markets; the limited area to which his meal-transportation advantages apply; and, temporarily, the unprofitable effects of the ceiling price of soybean meal in relation to the market price of soybeans and soybean oil. A preliminary appraisal seems to indicate, however, that the factors favoring a further expansion of the soybean industry in Minnesota outweigh those limiting its expansion.

SOURCE OF DATA

The data used in this study were obtained from producers, processors, and other segments in the industry; the Bureau of Agricultural Economics and the Fats and Oils Division of the Production Marketing Administration of the United States Department of Agriculture, the Federal-State Crop and Livestock Reporting Service, State Feed and Fertilizer Division; published material of the Divisions of Agronomy and Plant Genetics and Agricultural Economics, University of Minnesota; the Interstate Commerce Commission; the various railroads and their agricultural agents; the statistical department of Cargill, Incorporated; and George L. Levin, professional engineer. Valuable information and suggestions were also obtained during personal interviews

[1] The Minnesota processor usually quotes his purchase price for soybeans basis the Chicago market less freight to the point of production. The transportation section of Chapter V discusses this more fully.

[2] Both meal and oil prices are based on a Decatur market plus freight from Decatur to the point of sale. The section on transportation in Chapter V discusses this more fully.

with men in the grain trade and with officials of commodity markets (Appendix, p. 173).

PROCEDURE

The first part of the study deals with the growth and development of the soybean crop on world, national, and state levels. Special emphasis is placed on the comparative advantage of growing soybeans in Minnesota, as this seems to be the best means of evaluating the Minnesota producer's competitive position. The next part, Chapter III, deals with the utilization of the soybean crop and the processed products of meal and oil. It presents an analysis of the past, present, and future market potentials of soybeans, meal, and oil. Chapter IV concerns the development of the processing industry, the trends in technological progress, and the effects of technology on operation costs to the processor.

The fifth chapter sets forth the Minnesota processor's advantages in location. The analysis presented is primarily concerned with the interrelation of transportation, storage, commodity markets, and price formulation, and the impact of these factors on crushing margins, inasmuch as the crushing margin is the chief criterion in determining location advantage.

The final chapter consists of a brief summary and, in the light of the data previously presented, appraises the competitive position of the Minnesota soybean producer and processor.

CHAPTER II

Production

THE soybean, also called the soya bean, soja bean, and Manchurian bean, is an annual summer legume, native of Southeastern Asia.[1] Writings about this important crop date from 2838 B.C., in the ancient Chinese period of Emperor Sheng-Nung, to the present time. Despite its unusual food properties of protein and oil, the soybean spread slowly to other parts of the world. Missionaries in Asia sent various varieties of soybeans to Europe. These soybean seeds were planted in Paris as early as 1740, but the expansion of the crop in Europe was limited because the climatic conditions were not well suited to the development of the bean. The small production in Europe today centers in Russia, Austria, Yugoslavia, Hungary, Roumania, and Bulgaria.

The development of the soybean crop in America also was slow. The soybean was first mentioned in 1804, but not until 1898 were new varieties introduced and developed by the United States Department of Agriculture. The first intensive development occurred in the southeastern states of Virginia, Mississippi, Kentucky, and Alabama, about 1919. However, by 1924 the Corn Belt states had become the leading production area, accounting for over 40 per cent of the total soybean crop. Today over 75 per cent of the 280 million bushel crop is grown there.

The expansion of the industry during the late 1920's was only moderate, the total output of soybeans in 1930 amounting to 14 million bushels. However, in subsequent years, the expansion exceeded all expectations, the production increasing to 78 million bushels in 1940 and to 287 million bushels in 1950.

The main economic reasons for such a rapid increase in the soybean crop were as follows: the farmer's comparative advantage in growing

[1] W. A. Wheeler, *Forage and Pasture Crops*, pp. 404–411.

soybeans in his over-all farm operations; the increasingly high level of the national economy, together with the growth of the human and livestock population that provided an effective demand for protein and oil; the loss of important sources of fats and oils during the war and the mounting needs of our allies; and the postwar requirements of Europe for fats and oils, partially met by the use of E.C.A. funds. In addition, there were other circumstances favoring a rapid development of the soybean crop in the United States. They include: tariff protection; price supports; the relaxation of acreage controls; the production and technological research of the government, colleges, and industry; and the leadership of the American Soybean Association and the National Processors Association.

Not only has there been an increase in total soybean production, but also in facilities for processing and in technological improvements in processing and refining. The latter are of special significance because such improvements have resulted in a wide adaptability in the use of soybean products, particularly soybean oil.

WORLD PRODUCTION

A world record in soybean production was set in 1950 when the crop was estimated at 631.8 million bushels.[2] The harvest exceeded the previous high of 1948 by 12 per cent, the 1949 crop by 22 per cent, and the prewar average by 36 per cent (Appendix, Table 1). Growing over 45 per cent of the world's crop, the United States is now the world's leading soybean producer (Appendix, Table 1). China's estimated production of 179 million bushels in 1949 (about 30 million bushels below its prewar average) was probably exceeded in 1950 but not by nearly enough to reach the record United States crop of 287 million bushels. Manchuria, the third most important soybean-producing country, raised approximately 66 million bushels in 1949, or about 80 million bushels less than its prewar average production. The recent war in Korea has also lessened that country's soybean production. In 1949, Korea harvested approximately 6.5 million bushels, or roughly 10 million bushels less than its prewar production. The decrease in Asiatic production was more than offset by the 1950 United States soybean crop, which was almost 230 million bushels greater than the prewar average. Not only has production advanced in the United States, but

[2] Fats and Oils: *World Production and Trade in 1950* (Foreign Agricultural Circular, March 16, 1951), p. 8.

also soybean average yields per acre have increased 3.1 bushels, or 16.9 per cent over the average prewar yield (Appendix, Table 1). With the exception of Italy, the other soybean producing countries have not increased their acre yields.

The war in Asia and World War II brought about much of the change in soybean acreage throughout the suitable areas of production. With the entrance of the United States into the war and the loss of supplies from Asia, America undertook measures to increase the domestic production of oil-seed crops for its own use and the use of its allies. It succeeded extremely well, and shifted quickly from a net importing to an exporting country in the soybean and soybean oil world market (Appendix, Tables 2 and 3). This increased production by the United States was important not only because of the loss of regular vegetable protein and oil supplies but also because the blockade of Europe and the strain on British shipping resources brought about a cut in normal animal protein and fat supplies. The loss of butter supplies and the demand for fluid milk encouraged the expanding consumption of margarine in both the dairy and non-dairying countries.[3]

The changes in world soybean-production brought about during the war have been maintained and accelerated. Production in America has expanded because of the increasing needs of both the animal and human population in the domestic market and the E.C.A. purchases in the export market. Asiatic production has not returned to prewar levels because of internal strife in China and the Korean War. Consumption shifts from butter to margarine have also continued in the postwar period, the market for soybean oil thereby being enlarged. In addition, increased soybean-production in the United States was necessary to bring edible fat consumption up to prewar levels in this country and in Britain and Western Europe. The greatest potential demand for fats and oils is found in countries which do not have the means to pay American dollars for soybeans. Hence, if production is to continue to expand in the hard-currency country of America, this country will either have to subsidize the soft-currency markets through programs of the E.C.A. type or buy more of these countries' exports so that they may have the means to pay for the needed fats and oils.

Tariff restrictions have also played an important role in shifts in the

[3] The analysis of this shift and its effect on the soybean industry will be discussed more fully in Chapter III.

production of soybeans in different areas of the world. From 1930 to 1948, the United States had the following tariff rates on soybeans, soybean oil, and soybean meal:[4]

Soybeans	2 cents a pound
Soybean oil	3.5 cents a pound, but not less than 45 per cent ad valorem
Soybean meal	0.3 cents a pound

As of May 1951 the tariff rates are as follows:[5]

Soybeans	2 cents a pound
Soybean oil	3 cents a pound but not less than 22½ per cent ad valorem
Soybean meal	0.15 cents a pound

In essence, these tariff rates increased the cost of importing these commodities as follows: $1.20 a bushel (a bushel of soybeans is 60 pounds) for soybeans, 3 cents a pound for oil, and $3 a ton on soybean meal. However, it is not necessarily true that these rates were reflected fully in the national prices of these items. Naturally, other countries have import duties on these same items. Canada, for example, has tariff restrictions on soybean oil coming into the country, but not on soybeans or soybean meal.

Trade flows indicate even more strikingly the changes in world soybean-production and consumption that have occurred from the prewar to the postwar period (Figs. 4 and 5). Immediately preceding World War II America became a soybean exporting country, but Manchuria was by far the dominant exporter, accounting for an equivalent of over 90 million bushels. In the postwar period, the United States approached Manchuria's prewar trade dominance by exporting an equivalent of 78 million bushels in the 1950–1951 crop year.[6] Manchuria's chief markets were Western Europe, Japan, and Egypt; America's markets are Western Europe, Japan, and Canada.

If the Korean War is settled in the near future (present time of writing, March 1952), trade from the soft-currency area of Manchuria to the soft-currency area of Europe should increase. A notable growth occurred in shipments from Manchuria to Western Europe in spite of

[4] *U.S. Tariff Rates on Agricultural Products,* B.A.E., U.S. Department of Agriculture, Washington, D.C., May 1951.

[5] *Ibid.*

[6] *Soybean Digest,* December 1951, p. 33.

FIGURE 4. International Trade in Soybeans, Average for 1935–1939.

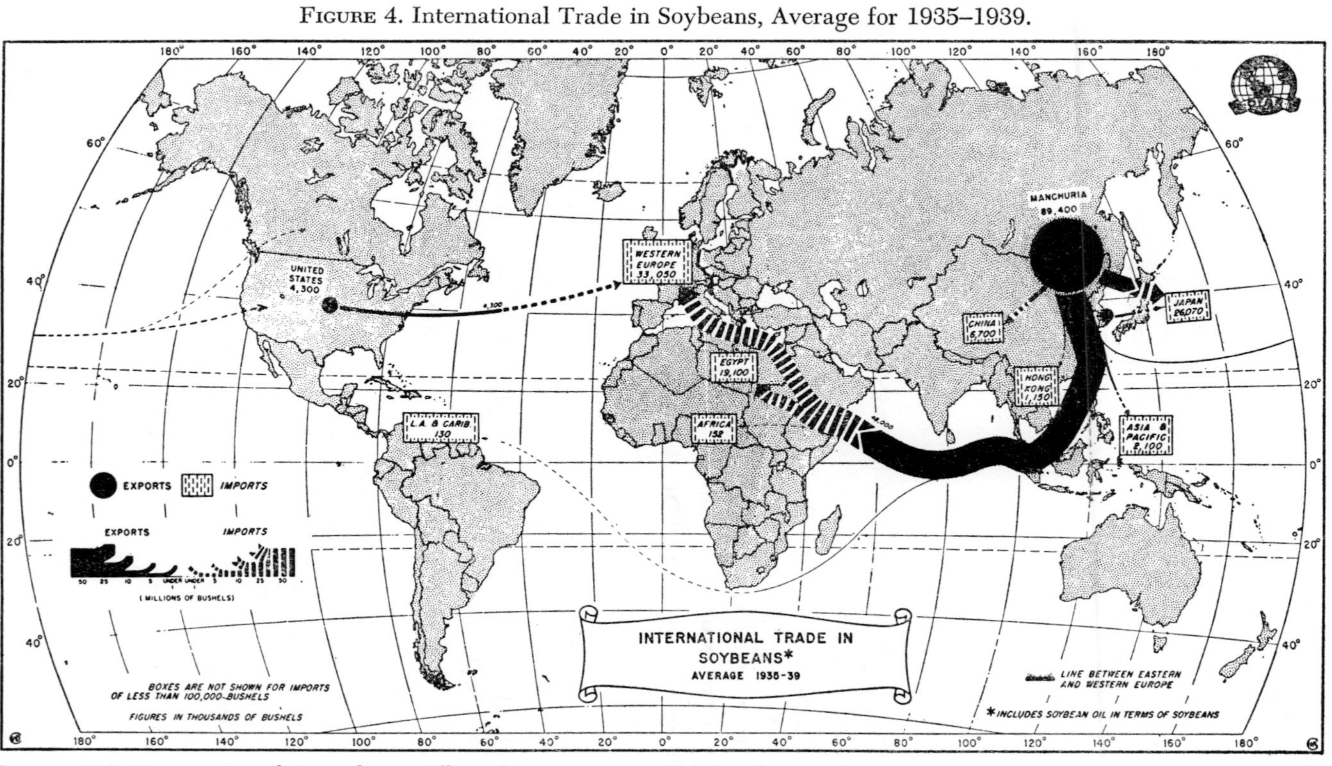

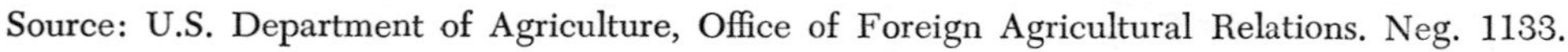
Source: U.S. Department of Agriculture, Office of Foreign Agricultural Relations. Neg. 1133.

FIGURE 5. International Trade in Soybeans, Average for 1948–1949.

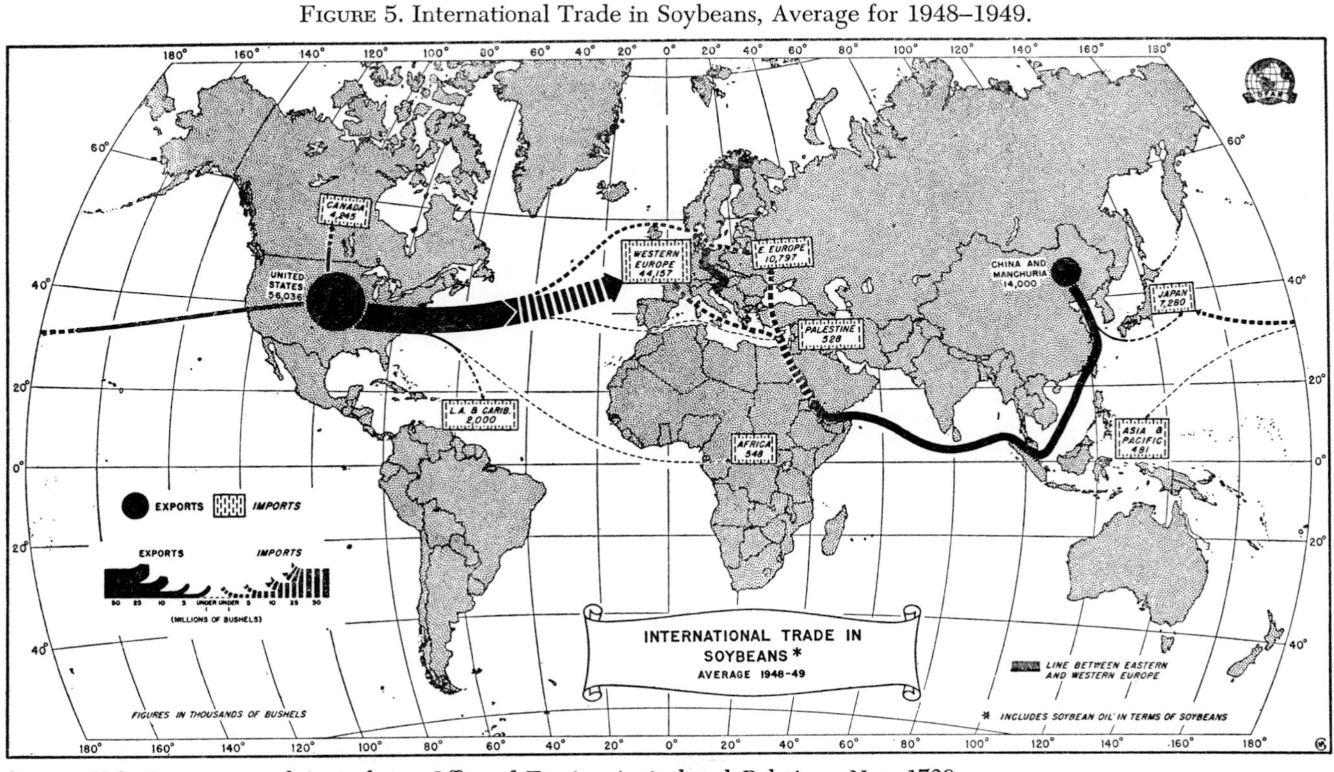

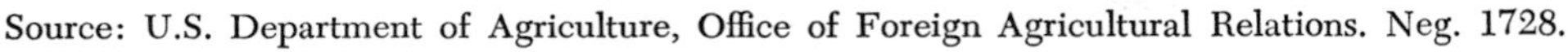
Source: U.S. Department of Agriculture, Office of Foreign Agricultural Relations. Neg. 1728.

the war in Korea (Appendix, Table 4). Further stimulus is given to the expansion of the exports from Manchuria by the United States grade standards. The United States grades are based on a contract grade of 3 per cent dockage and 14 per cent moisture, whereas the other trading countries of the world use a "fair average sample of the crop" as the deliverable grade. This average of the world crop usually contains less than 1 per cent dockage and approximately 10 per cent moisture. American growers and elevator operators tend to blend the crop to the maximum United States standards for dockage and moisture, and European purchasers naturally resent this.

In summary, world production of soybeans has increased in the last decade to a new world record. World War II provided the impetus to the rapid development of the crop in America and this intensive growth has continued in the postwar period in answer to the demands of a growing and prosperous national population and in answer to the needs of Europe. On the other hand, Asiatic soybean producers have not regained their production and markets of the prewar world because of the continued strife in China and Korea. However, a reversal of the shift apparently is in progress and will probably continue. The dollar shortages of importing countries, governmental trade restrictions, and poor competitive United States grade standards are all factors influencing foreign demand to shift back to Manchuria for soybeans. If peace does come, then Asia will be in a better position to increase its production for the world markets, and importers will be more disposed to buy from countries at peace.

NATIONAL PRODUCTION

The expansion of soybean production from a crop of less than 5 million bushels in 1925 to one of over 287 million bushels in 1950 resulted from several unique pressures on American agriculture and unusual responses to those pressures. The greatest production increases have occurred in the last ten years and more specifically between 1941 and 1942, the enormous impetus World War II gave to the development of the crop in this country thus being apparent (Appendix, Table 5). Before the war the United States was a net importer of oil seed crops for its animal feed and edible oil uses. The war cut off many of the Asiatic supplies to this country. At the same time rising incomes resulted in heavier demands for meat, which in turn meant a greater need of protein supplies to feed the expanding livestock numbers. Feed demand was further accentuated by the development of the mixed feed industry and its emphasis on new scientific formula feeds for all types of livestock. Likewise the oil market was strengthened because of the need to replace imported oils, the greater use of vegetable shortening, and the replacement of butter by margarine. These wartime demands together with high government support prices, relaxation of acreage controls, and increasing soybean yields brought about the rapid rise of the soybean crop during this period. However, this expansion was not created in a vacuum, and the historical development of the crop that made this wartime expansion possible indicates several trends that have an important bearing upon the competitive position of the Minnesota producer and processor of soybeans.

The early expansion of the crop in the 1920's took place in the southern and eastern states (Table 1). Crop rotations in some parts of the South included soybeans along with lespedeza, oats, and corn to help control the cotton boll weevil.[7] In the middle and late 20's, the production area shifted to the Corn Belt, with 40 per cent of the acreage located there. By 1940 over two thirds of the total soybean crop was produced in the Corn Belt, and by 1950 over three fourths.

By arbitrarily dividing states into specific geographical areas (Appendix, Table 6), the extreme dominance of the Corn Belt area is more clearly demonstrated despite fairly significant gains within the Lake states and Delta states (chiefly Minnesota and Arkansas).[8] The favorable soil and climatic conditions, the high yields and oil content of its soybeans, the local processing demand and livestock markets, as well as the unrestricted shipping area of the central location of Illinois have led to the predominant position of the Corn Belt in the production of soybeans.

Until 1941 over half of the acreage devoted to the soybean crop consisted of hay, grazing, or green manure usage (Appendix, Table 7). The Agricultural Adjustment Administration's soil-building program encouraged the use of soybeans as a green manure crop. At the same time soybeans, because of their late planting, were used as emergency forage crops to take the place of drought-damaged corn and small grain

[7] Edwin G. Strand, *Soybeans in American Farming* (U.S. Department of Agriculture, Technical Bulletin No. 966, November 1948), p. 4.

[8] For purposes of analysis, these areas are defined roughly as follows: Corn Belt: Illinois, Iowa, Indiana, Ohio, and Missouri; Lake states: Minnesota, Wisconsin, and Michigan; Delta states: Arkansas, Mississippi, and Louisiana.

TABLE 1. A Comparison of the Twelve Leading Soybean-Producing States for 1920 and 1950

State	Thousand Bushels	Percentage of Total U.S. Production
1920 Production of Soybeans *		
1. North Carolina	1,638	54.6
2. Virginia	570	19.0
3. Alabama	228	7.6
4. Missouri	133	4.4
5. Kentucky	120	4.0
6. Illinois	92	3.1
7. Ohio	64	2.1
8. Tennessee	50	1.7
9. Indiana	42	1.4
10. Wisconsin	28	0.9
11. Georgia	22	0.7
12. Mississippi	15	0.5
Total	3,002	100.0
1950 Production of Soybeans †		
1. Illinois	94,752	33.0
2. Iowa	42,262	14.7
3. Indiana	35,002	12.2
4. Missouri	27,393	9.5
5. Ohio	23,232	8.1
6. Minnesota	16,384	5.7
7. Arkansas	11,676	4.1
8. Mississippi	6,768	2.3
9. Kansas	6,462	2.3
10. North Carolina	5,117	1.8
11. Tennessee	3,150	1.1
12. Virginia	2,527	0.9
Total	274,725	95.7

* A. B. Paul, "Economic Factors in the Growth of the Oilseed Industry in the United States," unpublished Ph.D. thesis, University of Illinois, 1947.

† *Soybean Blue Book,* 1951.

crops in the 30's. The peak acreage thus used was 7 million acres in 1939 and 1940. Today this acreage is of less importance, consisting of 2 million acres of the 15 million acres devoted to soybeans (Appendix, Table 7).

Before 1935 the major utilizers of soybeans harvested for beans were seed companies and farmers who fed the beans to livestock. After 1935 the processing industry became the dominant user of the soybean (Appendix, Table 7). This fact is of special importance to the soybean grower of the North Central states as most of the "crushing" beans are located in this area. The southern and eastern sections use most of their soybeans for seed, for direct farm consumption, and for export.

Thus far, it has been demonstrated that the Corn Belt is the main production area of the soybean and that soybeans harvested for beans constitute the most significant portion of the total soybean acreage in these North Central states. Therefore, acreage changes and trends can best be analyzed by an examination of the acreage and production of soybeans harvested for beans in the Corn Belt states and Minnesota.

ACREAGE CHANGES IN THE CORN BELT

The early increases of soybean acreage in Illinois, Indiana, and Iowa were due primarily to decreases in small grains such as oats and wheat (Fig. 6). The oat acreage decreased in Iowa, and the wheat acreage declined in Indiana and Illinois. Some contraction of the corn acreage also occurred during the 30's. In more recent years there has been an increase in small grains (oats, wheat, and barley) as well as corn and soybeans, with decreases occurring in hay and pasture acreage (Fig. 6 and Appendix, Table 8). Hence, these more recent trends demonstrate that the State of Minnesota entered into the growing of soybeans after basic shifts in small grains had occurred in the principal soybean-producing states. Instead of displacing small grain crops, soybean acreage in Minnesota took the place of hay and pasture land during the war years.[9]

In addition to acreage changes among the Corn Belt states and Minnesota, yield and oil-content variations also play an important role in the production changes in these various states. Minnesota has one of the poorest records of all the leading soybean states in the per-acre bushel yield of soybeans (Appendix, Table 9). Consequently, it would seem likely that soybean production would not flourish in Minnesota. But such is not the case, and as will be shown later in this chapter, the comparative advantage of growing soybeans within the state has resulted in an increase in soybean acreage in Minnesota despite the low yields.

Not only are the bushel yields per acre low in Minnesota, but also soybeans produced in Minnesota are among the lowest in percentage of oil content, principally because of the low average temperature (Appendix, Tables 10 and 11).

[9] The significance of this shift will be discussed in the final section of this chapter.

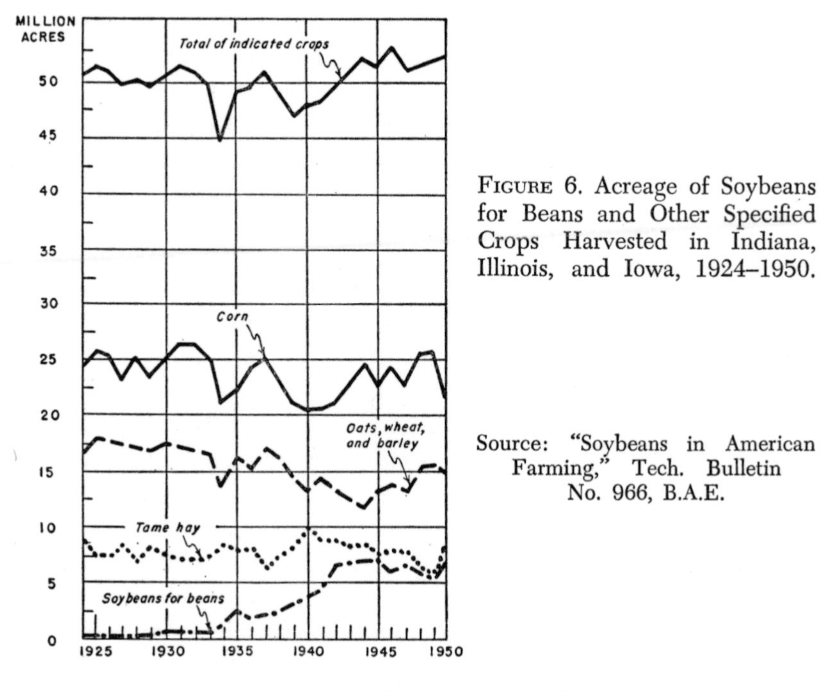

FIGURE 6. Acreage of Soybeans for Beans and Other Specified Crops Harvested in Indiana, Illinois, and Iowa, 1924–1950.

Source: "Soybeans in American Farming," Tech. Bulletin No. 966, B.A.E.

FIGURE 7. Map of the Ten Soybean-Producing Areas.

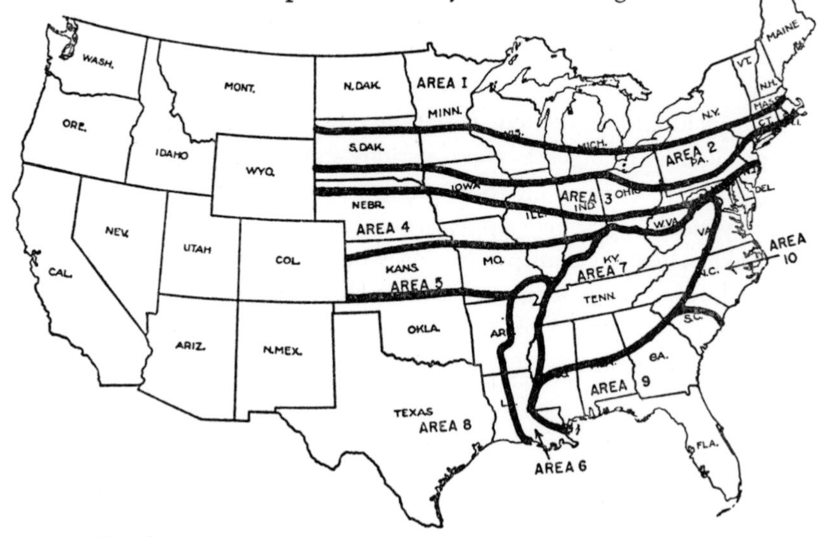

Source: "Marketing Study of the Oil Content of Soybeans as Related to Production Areas and Climate," P.M.A.

Figure 7 designates the ten main soybean-producing areas from north to south, Minnesota's production occurring primarily in Area 2. The protein content of the soybean and the iodine number[10] of the oil decrease from north to south (Areas 1 through 6) (Table 2). The oil content of the soybean increases from north to south, the high correlation between temperature and oil content thus being demonstrated (Table 2).

TABLE 2. A Summary of Protein Content, Oil Content, and Iodine Number of Soybeans, by Area, Three-Year Averages, 1945–1947 *

Area	Protein Percentage	Oil Percentage	Iodine Number
1	42.86	19.35	136.53
2	42.20	19.69	131.40
3	41.57	20.64	130.77
4	40.80	20.86	131.03
5	41.30	20.47	130.77
6	41.10	20.90	130.00
7	42.27	20.37	132.20
8	42.30	20.43	133.10
9	43.17	19.97	132.70
10	43.40	19.67	134.90

* Values computed from results of the Cooperative Uniform Soybean Tests, Part I and Part II, 1945, 1946, 1947.

Again, it would seem logical to assume that the low oil content of Minnesota soybeans would lessen the expansion of soybean production in Minnesota compared with the better situated Corn Belt states. Yet, this is not the situation. In fact, the strong market-demand by Minnesota and Iowa processing concerns for locally grown soybeans has failed to discount the Minnesota soybean crop by the full value of the oil content difference between Minnesota and Illinois soybeans.

Efforts to increase the yield and oil content of soybeans harvested for beans on the northern fringe area are looked at with dubious eyes by the processors of that region. They feel that the high correlation of temperature with oil content makes it difficult for new varieties to overcome this disadvantage. But with the development of varieties, such as

[10] The iodine number in oil measures its oxygen absorption power. The higher the iodine number, the more readily the oil absorbs oxygen and dries. Hence, high iodine numbers are preferred for the paint industry. The low iodine numbers are preferred for edible oil uses.

the Blackhawk, which yields well and has increased oil content, perhaps the processors will become more optimistic about the future expansion of the crop in Minnesota.

It seems evident from the previous discussion that increased national production of soybeans is dependent upon the price and yields of *local* competing crops in the areas of feasible soybean production and not upon the differences in yields and oil content of these production areas. Because the Corn Belt has had the greatest increase in soybean production, it would seem that the soybean-corn price ratio would be a reasonable indicator of the competitive position of soybeans in this area. The soybean-corn price ratio in the middle 30's was approximately 1.11 (1935); but by 1941 it rose to 2.06 and remained at a high level. The average ratio during World War II was 1.7 compared with 1.4 during 1935–1939 (Fig. 8).

FIGURE 8. Prices Received by Farmers for Soybeans, Corn, and Oats, United States, Season Average, 1924–1950.

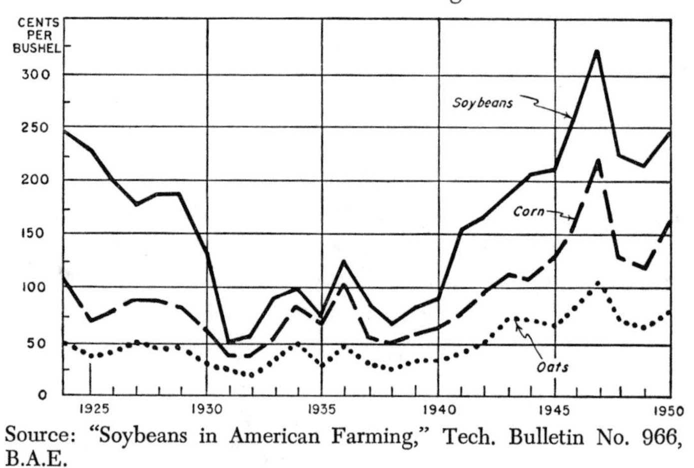

Source: "Soybeans in American Farming," Tech. Bulletin No. 966, B.A.E.

Other factors increasing the national production of soybeans are the mechanization that took place in the 40's, the value of the nitrogen of the crop in the farmers' over-all rotation program, the diversity of use if the seed crop fails to mature, and the lateness of planting to permit maximum flexibility in deciding when to grow the crop. The research activities by the agricultural experiment stations and the United States

FIGURE 9. Concentration of Soybean Production in the Various Types of Farming Areas in Minnesota, 1949–1950.

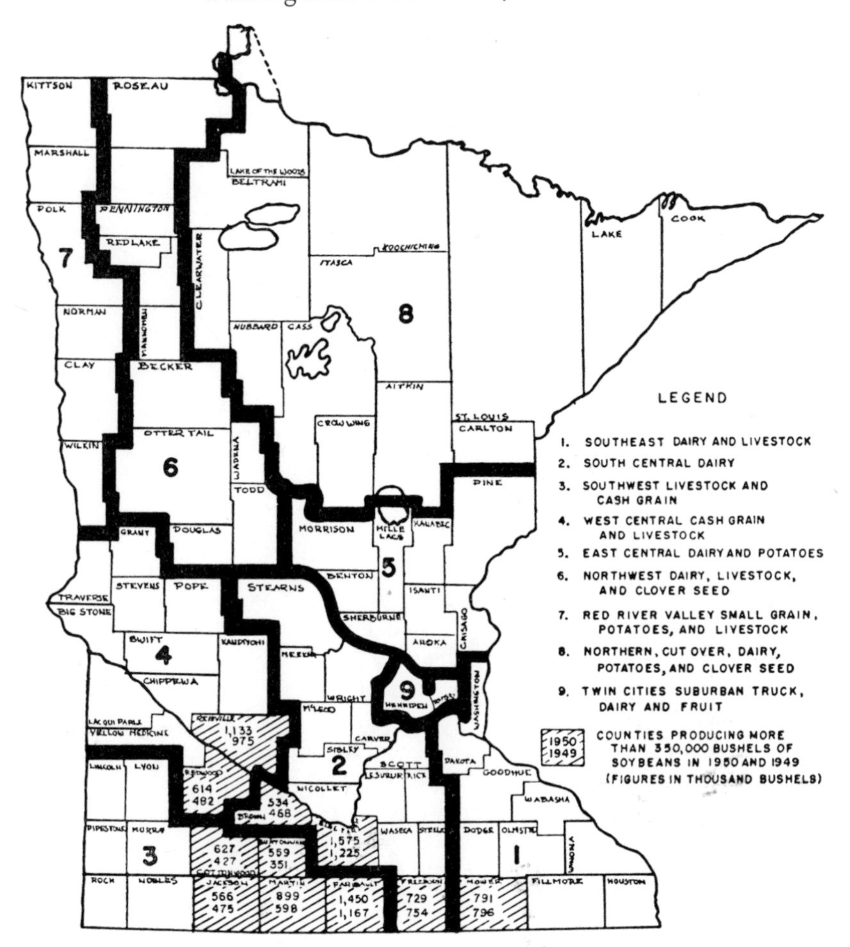

Department of Agriculture, as well as the beneficial educational policies of the industry, the American Soybean Association and the National Processors Association, have all aided the expansion of the crop in the United States.

World and national soybean-production trends have been examined. It is now feasible to discuss the development of the crop in Minnesota within this interrelated and interdependent national and international framework.

FIGURE 10. Types of Soils in Minnesota.

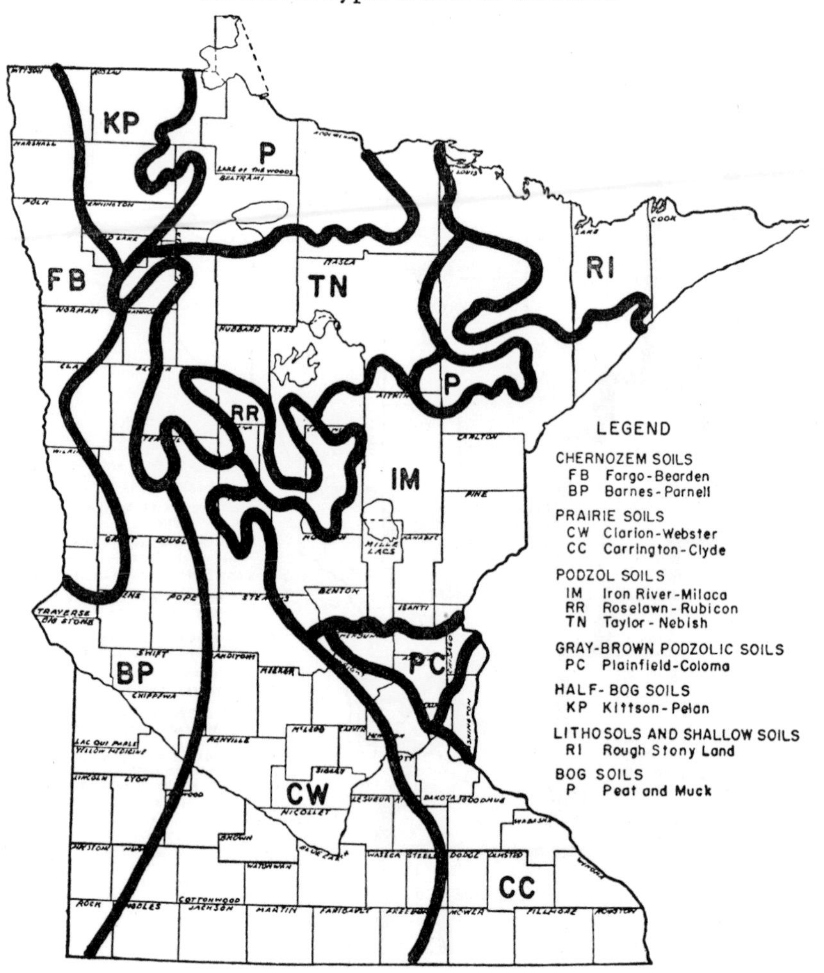

MINNESOTA PRODUCTION

Although raised as a minor forage crop during the depression years, it took a wartime economy and increased crushing capacity to develop soybeans as a crop harvested for beans in Minnesota.

AREAS OF PRODUCTION

Soybeans, like corn, are grown mainly in the southern third of the state, where the longer growing season, more abundant rainfall, and better prairie soils permit fairly profitable yields of the crop (Figs. 9 and 10). Eleven counties harvested over half the production of the state in 1949 and 1950, producing 7,719,836 bushels and 9,476,200 bushels respectively (Fig. 9).

In 1949 only 19 counties planted as much as 5 per cent of their tillable farm land to soybeans to be harvested for beans.[11] The percentage of tillable acreage given to soybeans by these counties is as follows:

County	Per cent	County	Per cent	County	Per cent
Blue Earth	15.3	Nicollet	8.3	Redwood	6.4
Faribault	13.2	Watonwan	8.0	Swift	6.1
Mower	13.0	Cottonwood	7.5	Dakota	5.9
Freeborn	11.0	Martin	7.2	Sibley	5.7
Renville	10.9	Waseca	7.1	Lac Qui Parle	5.6
Chippewa	10.4	Dodge	7.1		
Brown	9.0	Jackson	6.8		

These counties are distributed among four type-of-farming areas (Figs. 9 and 10). Areas 1 and 2 contain small dairy farms, with emphasis on the production of feed crops. Areas 3 and 4 are composed of larger farms, with meat production and cash crops as the important items. "The index of crop yields in these county groups based on the state average are: Area 1, 101; Area 2, 115; Area 3, 110; and Area 4, 92."[12]

SUITABLE VARIETIES

Having selected the location in Minnesota most suitable to the growing of soybeans, the farmer was faced with the problem of obtaining varieties that would be adaptable to the relatively short growing season. More than 10,000 soybean varieties have been introduced into America by the United States Department of Agriculture.[13] Most of them have come from Manchuria, Japan, Korea, China, Java, Sumatra, and India. However, only a few of these were adapted to Minnesota conditions.[14] The present varieties in Minnesota were introduced from other regions. The most prominent present variety is the Blackhawk.

Some of the desirable features needed for Minnesota soybean pro-

[11] George A. Pond, *Soybeans in the Minnesota Cropping System* (Tri-State Soybean Processors' Conference at Columbia, Mo., 1950).

[12] *Ibid.*

[13] W. A. Wheeler, *Pasture Crops.*

[14] J. W. Lambert, *Minnesota Farm and Home Science* (University of Minnesota, February 1949).

TABLE 3. The Results of Tests on Two Groups of Varieties of Soybeans

Variety	5-Year Yield, Bushels	1950 Yield, Bushels	Maturity, Days Earlier than Ottawa-Mandarin	Height, Inches	Oil Percentage
Group O (Varieties tested at St. Paul, Minnesota)					
Capital	27.2	29.1	−3	36	19.9
Hokiem	...	29.6	−2	38	19.8
Ottawa-Mandarin	28.3	24.9	0	34	17.4
Flambeau	23.4	24.9	−16	31	18.0
Pridesoy 57	...	21.4	0	31	17.3
Group I (Varieties tested at St. Paul, Minnesota, 1950)					
Blackhawk	...	22.6	6	38	19.0
Monroe	...	21.9	0	42	17.8
Earlyana	...	18.7	8	41	18.2
Habaro	...	14.8	14	35	16.6
Ottawa-Mandarin	...	21.2	0	32	17.1
Harly	...	20.4	8	43	16.4

duction are short maturity, good yields and high oil content, a uniform height for the use of the combine, tough seed coats that will not shatter when mature, and disease-resistant qualities. In Minnesota actual selections were made during the early part of the century, but a breeding program was not begun until World War II. Good hybridization takes from ten to fifteen years. Hence, new hybrid varieties that were bred in Minnesota are still not available and will not be for some time.[15]

Uniform soybean tests are conducted by the United States Regional Soybean Laboratory at Urbana, Illinois, in conjunction with various agricultural experiment stations. These tests are divided into area groupings: group O containing varieties adaptable to the Dakotas, Minnesota, and northern Wisconsin, and group I constituting strains suitable for southern Minnesota.[16] An examination of the known results of these two groups of tests of varieties partially indicates the potential development of improved soybean strains for use in Minnesota (Table 3). From this table, the Blackhawk would seem to be the most promising variety for southern Minnesota.

[15] Interview with Dr. Lambert (fall of 1951).

[16] *Results of the Cooperative Uniform Soybean Tests, 1950* (U.S. Regional Laboratory, Urbana, Illinois, March 1951). The data in Table 3 are derived from this source.

More recent information obtained from the annual reports of the University of Minnesota soybean-yield trials substantiates the development of new, improved, early-maturing varieties with high oil content (Table 4).[17]

TABLE 4. The Averages for Soybean Varieties for Date Mature and Oil Content at Three Locations, Waseca, Blue Earth, and Southwestern Minnesota

Variety	Date Mature	Oil Percentage
Ottawa-Mandarin	September 13	20.5
Habaro	September 22	19.3
Monroe	September 21	20.2
Blackhawk	September 25	20.7
Harly	September 23	19.6

The yields and oil content of soybeans naturally are also important to the processors of the crop. Such early processors as Mr. Riley Lewis, Mr. Frank Bergman, and Mr. Forrest E. Benson brought improved oil-bearing varieties into the state. They distributed these seeds to those farmers whom they considered to be the most progressive. No price differentiation was made between the old and new varieties, but the processor tried to obtain the better varieties in the state, and in addition bought Iowa-grown beans if they were more satisfactory than the locally grown crop.

The interdependent relation of processor and producer is pointed up by the following comment: "Soybean growers in southern Minnesota are becoming increasingly aware of the needs of crushing plants in selecting their varieties. Seed inquiries reveal a renewed interest in the Manchu variety. This follows publication of the fact that this variety is wanted by crushing plants because it averages nearly 2 per cent higher in oil content than Habaro, another common variety. Until last year, Habaro soybeans had been increasing in popularity because they are a few days earlier in maturity and showed more resistance to lodging. However, with the erection of a soybean plant at Mankato, farmers became conscious of soybeans as a cash crop. Consequently, high oil varieties are in greater demand."[18]

[17] H. K. Hayes, E. R. Ausemus, J. O. Culbertson, J. W. Lambert, and R. G. Robinson, *Varietal Trials of Farm Crops* (Miscellaneous Report 15, Agricultural Experiment Station, University of Minnesota, February 1952).

[18] Winfield Forsberg, *Soybean Digest*, March 1941, p. 10.

The interrelation between the producer and processor of soybeans will be discussed more fully in subsequent chapters.

ACREAGE CHANGES IN MINNESOTA

Having ascertained soil and climatic conditions and more adaptable varieties favorable to the growing of soybeans in Minnesota, the farmer next decided what crop, if any, soybeans should displace in Minnesota. One of the first studies made of the increased soybean production in Minnesota was that of Hugh A. Johnson.[19] In this study, the percentage change made in land use by forty-two southwestern farmers from 1941 through 1945 was found to be as set forth in Table 5.

TABLE 5. Percentage Changes in the Use of Land by Forty-two Minnesota Farmers, 1941 through 1945 (1940 = 100 per cent)

Crop	1941	1942	1943	1944	1945
Corn	+11	+10	+41	+47	+67
Soybeans for beans	+136	+503	+340	+380	+746
Flaxseed	+12	+26	+21	−47	−47
Other small grains	−58	−35	−42	−38	−23
Alfalfa hay	−7	+18	−8	−13	−14
Land operated	0	+4	+4	+18	+5

The actual changes in soybean acreage on these forty-two farms during the five years studied were only slight. The percentage changes fluctuated widely because of the small acreage devoted to soybeans on these farms in the base year of 1940. No straight-line trend toward an increase in production is discernible. The 1943 acreage declined from that in the 1942 crop year because of adverse weather conditions and the lack of experience in soybean farming on the part of Minnesota farmers. The sharp increase in 1945 was due to better returns per acre and excellent growing conditions for the 1944 crop.

Perhaps more revealing are the absolute changes in crop acreages in Minnesota counties with over 5 per cent of their tillable land in soybeans harvested for beans from 1939 to 1949 (Table 6).[20]

Soybean acreage increased the greatest amount, followed by corn

[19] Hugh A. Johnson, *The Future of Flax and Soybean Production in Southwestern Minnesota* (U.S. Department of Agriculture in cooperation with the Minnesota Agricultural Experiment Station, April 1946).

[20] George A. Pond, *Soybeans in the Minnesota Cropping System* (Tri-State Soybean Processors' Conference, 1950).

TABLE 6. Changes in Crop Acreages between 1939 and 1949

Crop	Number of Thousand Acres				
	Type-of-Farming Areas				
	1	2	3	4	Total
Corn					
1939	195	617	712	268	1,792
1949	246	780	788	323	2,137
Oats					
1939	179	430	470	214	1,293
1949	193	490	498	211	1,392
Hay and pasture					
1939	301	489	411	147	1,348
1949	240	293	235	137	905
Soybeans					
1939	11	5	5	0	21
1949	78	213	712	69	1,072
Flax					
1939	20	110	178	93	401
1949	20	110	186	125	441
Barley					
1939	50	206	222	94	572
1949	13	78	59	49	199
Wheat					
1939	27	124	44	136	331
1949	13	29	16	55	113
Rye					
1939	23	20	20	24	87
1949	5	9	5	7	26

acreage; slight gains were also made in oats and flax acreage. The decreases were largest in hay and pasture acreage, followed by barley acreage; wheat and rye acreage also declined. It seems evident from these data that hay and pasture, in general, have been displaced the most by the increased production of soybeans in Minnesota.

In order to ascertain more specifically the change that has occurred on individual farms, a study of fifty southern Minnesota farms was undertaken. The fifty farms selected were obtained from the University of Minnesota's Southwestern and Southeastern Minnesota Farm Management Service. The selection was based on longevity, and included all members in the Southwestern area with ten or more years of continuous records as well as members in the Southeastern area that had similar records and were located in counties having a relatively large acreage of soybeans.

It is evident that soybean acreage on these specified farms has increased relatively more than that of any other crop (Table 7). On the other hand, it is difficult to determine precisely what crops have been displaced by soybeans. The changes in the proportion of the tillable land in various crops on these fifty farms indicate several varying and inconsistent relationships (Table 8). The first major relative increase in soybean acreage on these farms occurred from 1941 to 1942. At the same time, corn and flax acreage also expanded. These acreage increases were counterbalanced by noticeable decreases in barley and oats acreage and smaller declines in hay and pasture acreage. The next significant soybean expansion took place from 1944 to 1945. The offsetting reduction occurred in corn, hay, and pasture acreage. The contraction of soybean acreage on these farms in 1946 was counterbalanced by the expansion of corn and hay acreage.

Corn and soybeans, because of their similar soil and climatic requirements, should compete with each other in acreage utilization; and in some of the previously cited shifts such was the case. But in the ten-year changes that have taken place on these fifty farms, both corn acreage and soybean acreage have increased (Table 7). The small grains, barley, wheat, and oats, taken together have a net increase for the ten-year period. Hence, unlike the Corn Belt shift to soybean acreage, the shift to soybeans on these selected farms cannot be explained by a displacement of small grains. The main shifts to soybeans on these fifty farms seem to be accounted for by a decrease in hay and pasture acreage (Table 7). However, in the acreage changes from 1949 to 1950, hay and pasture acreage increased along with soybean acreage. Therefore, despite the ten-year shift from hay and pasture acreage to soybean acreage, no consistent year-to-year pattern exists between increases in soybean acreage and decreases in the acreage of any particular crop.

The acreage changes for the State of Minnesota compared closely with those of the fifty farms studied (Tables 9 and 10). Soybean acreage expanded more uniformly in the state than was evidenced by the fifty-farm analysis. The largest decreases in the state were in hay acreage, as was true of the selected farms. However, from 1949 to 1950 the hay acreage in the state has expanded along with the soybean acreage, a fact that emphasizes the difficulty of assuming that any specific crop will be displaced by soybeans.

The fluctuating and conflicting acreage changes that have been illustrated in the preceding paragraphs and tables indicate the complex

TABLE 7. Index Numbers (by Percentage) of Acreage on Fifty Southern Minnesota Farms, 1941 through 1950 (1941 = 100 per cent)

Year	Flax	Barley	Oats	Wheat	Rye	Corn	Soybeans	Hay	Pasture	Not Cropped Tillable Land	Tillable Land	Total Land in Farms
1941	100.0	100.0	100.0	100.0	100.0	100.0	100.0	100.0	100.0	100.0	100.0	100.0
1942	120.0	77.8	87.4	144.8	109.3	110.6	182.8	101.7	95.1	53.3	103.0	104.7
1943	104.5	40.8	90.5	82.0	45.2	139.1	136.2	85.1	99.3	121.0	105.3	106.3
1944	42.1	11.4	101.4	78.2	113.0	131.8	145.9	88.7	94.1	472.5	105.4	107.3
1945	47.5	11.6	128.7	86.6	101.7	115.7	364.7	72.4	91.0	199.3	106.2	108.1
1946	42.3	36.0	114.8	132.9	186.4	131.7	228.8	74.5	81.9	52.6	98.4	99.8
1947	80.9	44.6	107.9	82.2	169.5	123.8	280.5	73.9	80.8	239.0	100.7	102.2
1948	106.1	60.3	113.8	76.3	542.4	129.9	239.3	75.5	71.0	32.7	104.2	104.7
1949	78.3	79.8	117.0	39.9	45.2	146.4	206.2	77.7	75.2	66.2	106.9	106.9
1950	67.2	89.8	82.2	96.4	265.5	120.5	238.1	87.0	82.6	45.6	104.9	103.8

TABLE 8. Percentage of Total Tillable Land in Specified Crops on Fifty Southern Minnesota Farms, 1941 through 1950

Year	Flax	Barley	Oats	Wheat	Rye	Corn	Soybeans	Hay	Pasture	Not Cropped Tillable Land	Other	Tillable Land
1941	9.7	7.3	17.7	1.0	0.2	24.6	2.7	17.5	11.6	1.3	6.4	100.0
1942	11.3	5.5	15.0	1.3	1.0	26.4	4.9	17.2	10.7	0.7	6.0	100.0
1943	9.6	2.8	15.2	0.7	0.1	32.5	3.5	14.1	11.0	1.5	9.0	100.0
1944	3.9	.8	17.0	0.7	0.2	30.8	3.8	14.7	10.4	5.7	12.0	100.0
1945	4.3	.8	21.4	0.8	0.2	26.8	9.4	11.9	10.0	2.4	12.0	100.0
1946	4.2	2.7	20.6	1.3	0.3	33.0	6.4	13.2	9.7	0.7	7.8	100.0
1947	7.8	3.3	18.9	0.8	0.3	30.3	7.6	12.8	9.3	3.0	5.9	100.0
1948	9.9	4.2	19.3	0.7	0.9	30.7	6.3	12.7	7.9	0.4	7.0	100.0
1949	7.1	5.5	19.3	0.4	0.1	33.7	5.3	12.7	8.2	0.6	7.1	100.0
1950	6.2	6.3	20.5	0.9	0.4	28.3	6.2	14.5	9.1	0.6	7.0	100.0

TABLE 9. Tillable Land and Specified Crops in Minnesota

Crop	Number of Thousand Acres	Yield, Bushels per Acre	Production, Million Bushels
Flax			
1939–1948 Av.	1,320	10.1	13.5
1949	1,628	10.0	16.3
1950	1,205	11.0	13.3
Barley			
1939–1948 Av.	1,261	26.6	34.1
1949	1,061	24.0	25.5
1950	1,252	29.0	36.9
Oats			
1939–1948 Av.	4,548	37.6	171.6
1949	4,952	37.0	183.2
1950	5,101	37.0	188.7
Spring wheat			
1939–1948 Av.	1,094	17.3	18.8
1949	1,105	15.5	17.1
1950	774	17.0	13.2
Rye			
1939–1948 Av.	220	13.5	3.0
1949	170	15.0	2.6
1950	162	14.5	2.3
Corn			
1939–1948 Av.	5,087	42.2	214.4
1949	5,648	44.0	248.5
1950	5,111	38.0	194.2
Soybeans			
1939–1948 Av.	377	15.4	6.0
1949	709	18.0	12.8
1950	1,057	15.5	16.4
Hay			
1939–1948 Av.	4,351	...	....
1949	3,625	...	....
1950	3,812	...	....

TABLE 10. Percentage of Total Tillable Land in Specified Crops in Minnesota

Year	Flax	Barley	Oats	Wheat	Rye	Corn	Soybeans	Hay	Total
1939–1948 (total tillable acreage, 18.3 million acres)	6.3	6.0	21.7	5.2	1.0	24.2	1.8	20.7	86.9
1949 (total tillable acreage, 18.9 million acres)	7.8	5.1	23.6	5.3	0.8	26.9	3.4	17.3	90.0
1950 (total tillable acreage, 18.5 million acres)	5.7	6.0	24.3	3.7	0.8	24.3	5.0	18.2	88.0

variables that a farmer has to examine in order to determine the comparative advantage of growing soybeans. Some of the reasons farmers gave for growing soybeans for beans, together with the number giving that reason, are tabulated below:[21]

Reason	*Number*	*Percentage of Total Number*
Good price	22	33
Catch crop in wet year	18	27
Weed control (except cockle-burr)	7	11
Fits well in rotation	7	10
Use as a cash crop on fields not needed for feed	8	12
Use as a cultivated crop around corn fields of hybrid corn for seed	2	3
Grows better than most crops on spring plowing	1	2
Takes less labor	1	2
Total	66	100

The above indicates that price is the main reason given for growing soybeans in Minnesota.

Table 11, which designates the yearly value per acre of grain crops in the nineteen Minnesota counties that have over 5 per cent of their tillable land in soybeans, bears out the importance of the price factor in the farmer's decision to grow soybeans. In five of the ten years from 1940 through 1949 the value per acre of soybeans in these counties was second only to that of corn.

The comparative cost and returns per acre for grain crops in southern Minnesota are shown in Table 12. This study does not include some of the recent high soybean prices and, therefore, indicates a less favorable net income position for soybeans. Also the soybean prices used are obtained from all of southern Minnesota rather than from specific soybean-producing counties.

The excellent price received for soybeans has enabled it to rank fourth in dollar value in 1950 as a farm crop in Minnesota, even though it ranked fifth in percentage of total tillable land that same year (Fig. 11 and Table 10). The 1951 soybean crop in Minnesota was exceeded

[21] Hugh A. Johnson, *The Future of Flax and Soybean Production in Southwestern Minnesota* (U.S. Department of Agriculture in cooperation with Minnesota Agricultural Experiment Station, April 1946).

TABLE 11. The Dollar Value per Acre of Grain Crops in Southern Minnesota *

Year	Corn	Flax	Soybeans	Wheat	Barley	Oats	Rye
1940	$22.19	$15.84	$16.62	$14.88	$11.77	$10.91	$6.67
1941	30.32	20.45	24.33	13.74	16.31	10.40	6.36
1942	36.43	25.68	20.53	24.34	20.33	20.01	9.22
1943	43.55	28.87	25.76	25.10	19.41	23.30	12.19
1944	41.02	23.89	35.33	25.76	21.08	23.59	11.89
1945	41.79	34.25	31.66	31.22	32.89	29.37	26.24
1946	65.30	44.38	48.04	41.75	44.88	28.89	31.97
1947	80.48	72.03	53.11	46.00	58.43	39.68	37.68
1948	69.56	70.75	46.08	39.88	38.58	31.83	23.85
1949	51.30	38.52	38.96	33.68	31.08	23.11	19.08
Average rank	1.1	2.5	2.8	4.3	4.5	6.0	6.8

* Source: George A. Pond, *Soybeans in the Minnesota Cropping System* (Tri-State Soybean Processors' Conference, 1950).

TABLE 12. The Comparative Cost and Returns per Acre for Grain Crops in Southern Minnesota, 1945–1949 *

	Corn	Flax	Barley	Soybeans	Wheat	Oats	Rye
Average yield	44.8	10.4	28.0	17.4	17.4	38.0	15.9
Average price	$1.37	$4.47	$1.42	$2.26	$2.03	$0.73	$1.72
Value of crop	$61.38	$46.49	$39.76	$39.32	$35.32	$27.74	$27.35
Cost	25.23	27.52	24.77	25.00	26.98	23.79	25.17
Net return	$36.15	$18.97	$14.99	$14.32	$ 8.34	$ 3.95	$ 2.18

* Source: George A. Pond, *op. cit.*

in value only by corn and oats. The value of the corn crop was $322,-557,000; of oats $170,210,000; and of soybeans $50,890,000.[22]

Naturally, the price of soybeans, which has been the dominant element in the development of the crop in Minnesota, is dependent upon conditions of demand and supply in the world and in the nation. Consequently the resurgence of Manchuria as an important supplier of soybeans and the surplus oil supplies in this country are factors which will affect the price and production of Minnesota soybeans. In addition, soybeans are now in an unfavorable price relation with corn. Soybean prices generally tend toward a 2 to 1 price ratio with corn prices. Today corn is approaching a $2 per bushel price at Chicago, whereas soybean prices are approaching $3 a bushel (March 1952). This may mean a

[22] *Soybean Digest*, February 1952, p. 8.

FIGURE 11. Cash Receipts by Commodities, Minnesota, 1949–1950.

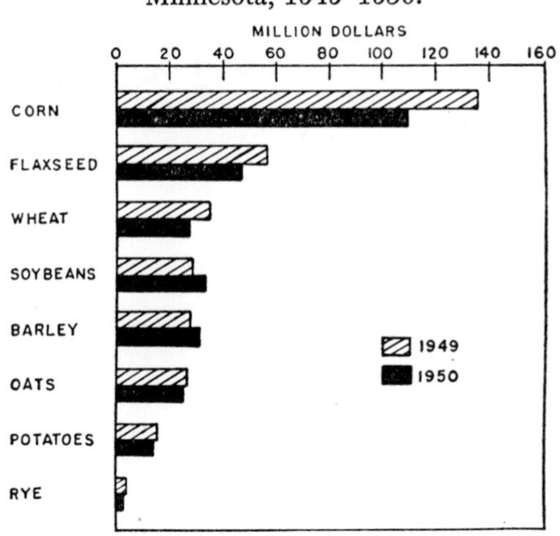

Source: Minnesota Agricultural Statistics 1949–1950, State Federal Crop and Livestock Reporting Service, p. 4.

shrinkage of soybean production in the dominant corn-producing states.[23]

However, past and future soybean production in Minnesota cannot be judged by price relationships alone. The large decrease in hay and pasture acreage was in part due to the loss of many young farmers to the armed services and defense plants during the war years. The labor cost of combining a field of soybeans was much less than that of obtaining a hay crop. Despite new types of balers and hay-making equipment, labor costs in harvesting a hay crop were not reduced as much through mechanization as were the costs of handling corn, soybeans, and small grains through the use of the combine. With the increased use of commercial high protein feeds, less hay and pasture land was used.

In addition, soybeans, because of their late planting date, can be seeded at the last moment. Therefore, if the first cutting of a hay crop proves to be a poor one, soybeans can be substituted. Or if the land is too wet in the spring to plant other crops, soybeans may be planted later when it is possible to get into the fields.

[23] *Ibid.*

TABLE 13. The Indicated Frequency with Which Forty-seven Selected Farms Produced Soybeans, 1941–1950 *

Simple Frequency			Cumulative Frequency		
Years	Number of Farmers Reporting	Percentage of 47 Farmers Reporting	Years	Number of Farmers Reporting	Percentage of 47 Farmers Reporting
1	4	8.5	1 or more	47	100.0
2	9	19.2	2 or more	43	91.5
3	2	4.2	3 or more	34	72.3
4	6	12.8	4 or more	32	68.1
5	8	17.0	5 or more	26	55.3
6	3	6.4	6 or more	18	38.3
7	4	8.5	7 or more	15	31.9
8	5	10.6	8 or more	11	23.4
9	3	6.4	9 or more	6	12.8
10	3	6.4	10 or more	3	6.4

* These farms are identical farms from year to year and are selected from those included in the Southeastern and Southwestern Minnesota Farm Management Service.

TABLE 14. The Number and Percentage of Fifty Southern Minnesota Farms Producing Soybeans

Year	Number of Farms	Percentage
1941	20	40
1942	27	54
1943	20	40
1944	16	32
1945	25	50
1946	26	52
1947	26	52
1948	27	54
1949	22	44
1950	25	50

TABLE 15. Soybean Acreage and Soybean Farms in Minnesota

	Total Number	Number Growing Soybeans	Percentage Growing Soybeans
Farms			
1944	181,403	15,173	8.4
1949	120,463	34,334	20.1
Acres			
1944	18,558,711	243,151	1.3
1949	19,709,121	753,305	3.8

Other factors, such as soil building, the alternative of using soybeans as a hay crop if the beans do not mature, the availability of corn equipment that can be used equally well for soybeans, and the suitability of soybeans in the over-all farm program have encouraged the Minnesota farmer to devote more of his land to soybean production.

The increases in soybean acreage that occurred in Minnesota were due to more farmers growing soybeans and to an expansion in soybean acreage by established soybean farmers. The study of the fifty southern Minnesota farms indicated that forty-seven of them produced soybeans one or more years from 1941 to 1950 (Table 13). A majority of them produced soybeans over half of the ten-year period. However, only 6.4 per cent of them produced soybeans all ten years. This lack of consistent soybean production in the farm's over-all rotation is further evidenced by the fact that only 54 per cent of these farms produced soybeans the same year (Table 14). Even though there was no general increase in the number of farms producing soybeans each particular year in this study, soybean acreage did increase during the ten-year period; thus, a larger acreage per farm must have been devoted to soybeans.

An analysis of the number of farms producing soybeans in the state and of the soybean acreage during this period (1944–1949) gives further evidence that an expansion in the number of farmers growing soybeans has occurred along with the increase in the soybean acreage of established soybean farmers (Table 15). The number of farms producing soybeans for beans from 1944 to 1949 increased from 8.4 per cent to 20.1 per cent of the total farms in Minnesota. Soybean acreage expanded from 1.3 per cent of the total crop land harvested in 1944 to 3.8 per cent in 1949. Using 1944 as the base period for the number of farms producing soybeans and the acreage given to soybeans, the number of farms increased 140 per cent and the soybean acreage expanded 190 per cent in the five-year period.

SUMMARY

The world production of soybeans is at its highest level in history. Although strife in China and Korea has curtailed the production of the crop in these countries, the United States has more than offset their declines. World War II provided the impetus for increased American soybean production. In spite of the continued conflict in Asia during the postwar period, Manchuria has begun to regain the export markets that she lost during World War II. American production has increased even more during the postwar period because of the strong national market and the subsidized foreign market for fat and protein.

National production, which responded to war and postwar demands, has been concentrated in the Corn Belt area. The basic acreage shift in this area was from small grain production to soybean production. Despite the Corn Belt's advantage in climatic and soil conditions, soybean expansion has also taken place in Minnesota. The principal causes of the increased production of soybeans in Minnesota have been price and other factors that have increased the comparative advantage of soybeans. The main acreage change in this state has been from hay and pasture acreage to soybean acreage. However, there is contrary evidence that this shift is not necessarily a normal and continuing one. Climatic and soil conditions limit the production of the soybean crop to principally the southern third of the state. New varieties that are now being developed for Minnesota may increase the intensity of production within the present growing area and lead to further expansion of the crop in other areas of the state.

Price measures the impact of the national and world supply of and demand for soybeans upon the Minnesota producer. The response of Minnesota producers to the price in turn affects the supply of soybeans. Having examined the production of soybeans, therefore, one must also analyze the markets for soybeans, meal, and oil in order to ascertain more clearly the competitive position of the Minnesota producer as well as the competitive position of the Minnesota soybean processor.

CHAPTER III

Utilization

WORLD UTILIZATION

The consumption of soybeans and soybean oil in the main importing countries of Western Europe has been maintained because of the expansion of the crop in the United States. The dollar shortage of these countries, however, has made them dependent upon E.C.A. funds for their purchases of soybeans and soybean oil in this country (Fig. 12). The E.R.P. countries received over 63.8 per cent of the total United States' soybean-equivalent exports in 1951 (Fig. 13).

The other important soybean importing countries, Japan, Spain, and Canada, have also relied upon American soybean production in the postwar period. Japan has been a major market because the Korean conflict and the Russian influence in China have made it difficult politically to trade with her soybean-producing neighbors. In addition, American dominance in the postwar administration of Japan has encouraged the purchase of soybeans from this country through the use of economic aid. The state of Minnesota has profited by the abnormal soybean market of Japan because of its location and transportation advantages.[1] However, the Japanese market will soon be lost because it is extremely uneconomical to transport soybeans and soybean oil from the United States across the Pacific Ocean when supplies are available in Japan's own immediate trading area. Even if better relations are not developed between communist Asia and the United States, the Japanese government has stated that it will return to the more normal prewar trade relations it had with its fellow Asiatic countries. Of course, Russian domination may prevent the resumption of normal trade between Japan and the soybean-producing countries of Asia at the present time.

[1] This will be discussed more fully in the final section of this chapter.

FIGURE 12. Destination of Exports of Soybeans and Soybean Oil from the United States under the Economic Cooperation Administration: April 3, 1948–June 30, 1951.

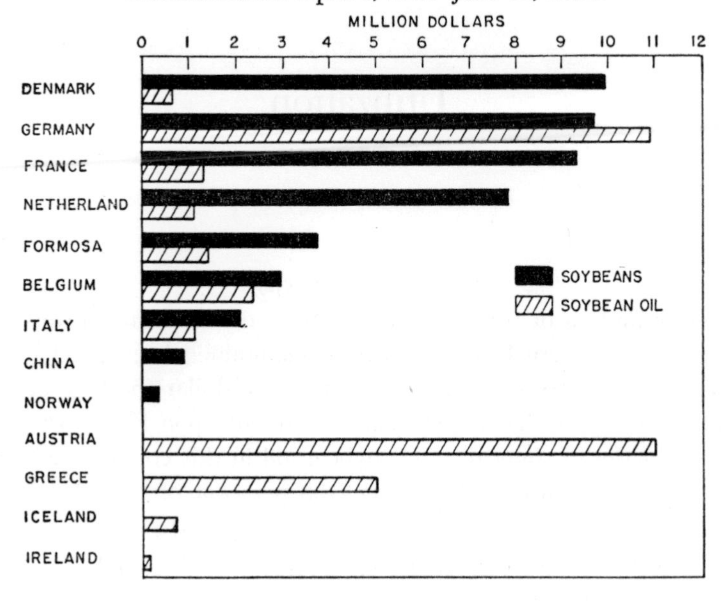

FIGURE 13. United States Exports of Soybeans (soybeans and oil as bean equivalent).

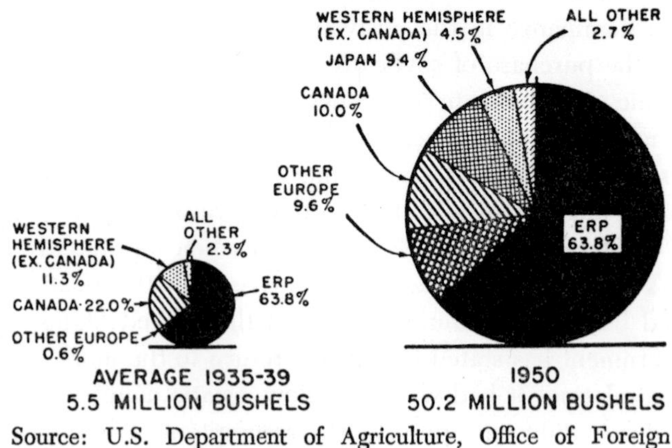

Source: U.S. Department of Agriculture, Office of Foreign Agricultural Relations. Neg. 1682-0.

TABLE 16. Canada: Soybeans Crushed, Soybean Oil, Cake and Meal Production, 1950, with Comparisons *

Year	Soybeans Crushed, Bushels	Soybean Oil Production, Short Tons	Oilcake and Meal Production, Short Tons
1945	1,057,683	4,573	24,420
1946	1,740,483	8,038	38,751
1947	2,423,383	12,071	54,484
1948	2,449,700	12,460	55,383
1949	4,508,133	22,982	105,314
1950	5,647,817	28,466	134,532

* Dominion Bureau of Statistics, "Report on the Vegetable Oil Industry in Canada, 1949," *Coarse Grains Quarterly,* February 1951.

TABLE 17. Canada: Imports of Soybeans, Edible and Inedible Soybean Oil, 1950, with Comparisons *

Year	Soybeans, Bushels	Soybean Oil, Short Tons	
		Edible	Inedible
1945	1,311,417	1,746	30
1946	1,135,650	6,048	28
1947	1,457,233	3,982	64
1948	1,445,300	2,885	64
1949	2,142,217	4,248	952
1950	4,004,367	2,334	1,967

* Dominion Bureau of Statistics, *Trade of Canada* (Foreign Agriculture Circular, May 3, 1951, O.F.A.R., U.S. Department of Agriculture), p. 3.

Spain is another abnormal market. The consumption of edible oil in Spain is largely dependent upon the Mediterranean olive-oil–producing countries. The olive crop in 1950 was below average; Spain, therefore, imported soybean oil from the United States in significant quantities for the first time in 1951. In 1951 the production of the olive crop was increased, with the resultant loss of the Spanish and other Mediterranean markets. The low price of soybean oil in the United States in the early months of 1952 demonstrates the weakened world edible-oil market.

On the other hand, Canada is an expanding market for soybeans and soybean oil (Tables 16 and 17). The crushing capacity of the country has increased rapidly in the last few years, especially since 1949, when Canada repealed a law prohibiting the manufacture and sale of margarine. Margarine production and consumption have proved to be an important outlet for Canadian soybean-oil production. The processing industry has increased the imports of soybeans from the United States, and the demand for soybean oil in Canada is strong enough to make it feasible to import oil even though there is a tariff on it (Table 17). Minnesota, because of its proximity to Canada, has supplied much of the Canadian imports of soybeans.

With the exception of Canada and the United States, the actual demand of the chief soybean-utilizing countries is very limited because of their difficult foreign exchange situation. Potentially, however, they have the greatest needs. The postwar fat percentage of total calories consumed in countries such as the United Kingdom, Germany, Netherlands, Denmark, and Japan is less than the prewar levels. In addition, over-all food levels of much of the world, including fat consumption per person, are extremely low. In the dairying countries the total visible edible fat per person is below prewar levels in spite of the spectacular increase in margarine consumption per person. This increase in margarine consumption during the war and postwar period is one of the reasons why soybean oil was probably the biggest factor in the world export market of edible oils in 1951. In essence, all the fats and oils available in the soft-currency areas have been consumed, and the surplus supplies remain in the hard-currency area or in communist-dominated countries. Therefore, the surplus of edible oils in the United States has to be contrasted with the inadequate diets of large segments of the most advanced countries as well as with the low levels of living of the population of the underdeveloped areas.

The increased use of margarine noted in the above discussion of actual and potential world utilization of soybean products has occurred in the countries which have subsidized the price of butter as well as in those countries which have subsidized the price of margarine. England has subsidized the price of butter more than that of margarine, as evidenced by the retail price index relationships between 1949 and the prewar period, yet margarine consumption has increased in the United Kingdom.[2] The Netherlands and Norway have subsidized margarine

[2] Butter was not singled out among foods to be subsidized in England. It is interesting to note that margarine consumption per capita was more than butter consumption per capita even though the rations allowable for each in England were the same. The industrial consumption of margarine affects this relationship, but no exact industrial data were obtained for this study.

in order to export butter more freely, with the result that margarine consumption has also increased in these dairy countries.

In addition to the increased consumption of products utilizing soybean oil in these Western European countries, the livestock industry has been expanding, which means a greater need for high protein feeds such as soybean meal. Soybean meal, however, because of its bulkiness and tendency to deteriorate over time, is fairly limited in its movement through international trading channels. Furthermore, these countries use grassland to a large extent to feed their cattle, and use potatoes foı hog production. The growing of feed grains is subsidized heavily in areas where production of them is possible, and this acts as a further limitation upon the use of imported soybean meal.

Most of these Western European countries have idle processing capacity that has remained relatively dormant during the war and postwar period. Consequently they would prefer to import soybeans and process their own oil and meal in order to build up their own internal economies. This situation might lead to an increased demand for American soybeans and a decreased demand for American soybean oil. The result may be higher soybean prices in America relative to meal and oil prices – in other words, a lower crushing margin for the American processor.

Finally, the significance of the foreign market cannot be measured by the soybean crop alone. Other edible oils, such as cottonseed oil, coconut oil, palm oil, peanut oil, corn oil, and olive oil, are substitutable; hence, a shortage or surplus of one of these oils affects the supply and demand of all the others. The actual world utilization of American soybeans and soybean oil has been large only because we have given these importing countries the financial means to realize a portion of their potential demand. The world utilization of soybeans, soybean oil, soybean meal, and their competing products plays an important part in the competitive position of the American soybean producer and processor and in turn in the competitive position of the Minnesota soybean producer and processor.

NATIONAL UTILIZATION

Protein and fat are the most important constituents of the soybean. The remaining ingredients are carbohydrates, moisture, ash, and some vitamins. All of these are needed in human and animal nutrition.

Most people prefer to obtain the protein in their diet through the

FIGURE 14. The Soybean: Uses – Derivatives – Applications.

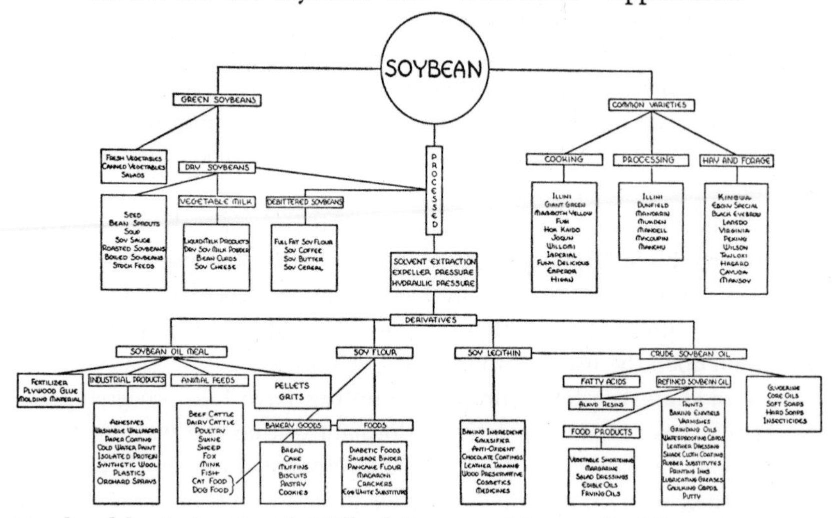

Developed by Archer-Daniels-Midland Company, Minneapolis, Minnesota

consumption of meat. Soybean meal, therefore, with its high protein content, is fed to livestock rather than to human beings directly. From a 60-pound bushel of soybeans, a range of 50½ pounds to 48 pounds of soybean meal is obtained, depending upon the manufacturing process and the oil and moisture content of the soybean. The other main product procured from the crushing process is soybean oil. A range of 10½ pounds to 8 pounds of oil is obtained from a bushel of soybeans. This oil or fat derived is of relatively low iodine number; consequently its primary use is in the edible market. The principal uses of the oil in the edible market are shortening, margarine, and salad dressings.

There are countless ways in which the soybean is utilized (Fig. 14), but these multiple uses have been overemphasized to the point where the main products of the soybean (meal and oil) are not thought of by the public. The chief products of the soybean must be examined in their principal roles of edible vegetable oil and high-protein livestock feed-supplement in order to ascertain some of the long-run demand trends of importance to the producer and processor of soybeans.

SOYBEAN MEAL UTILIZATION

The prewar production of soybean meal was approximately 1,300,000 tons, but by 1950 the United States was producing 5,300,000 (Fig. 15

and Appendix, Table 12). The largest gains in meal production in the last five years have been made in the states of Illinois, Iowa, Ohio, Missouri, and Minnesota (Fig. 15). The most recent actual consumption figures, obtained in 1945, when the industry was on a contract basis with the government, indicate the wide distribution of soybean meal, some being consumed in every one of the forty-eight states (Fig. 15 and Table 18). The state-to-state movement of soybean meal from the six principal meal-producing states re-emphasizes the national utilization of the product (Appendix, Table 13). Illinois, because of its central

FIGURE 15. Distribution of Soybean Meal in 1945 and Production of Soybean Meal in 1950, by States. (The figures within the states are in thousand tons. The top figure represents distribution. In those states in which no production figure is indicated, the production was less than 18 thousand tons, or a total of 386.9 thousand tons for all such states.)

location, large production, and Decatur pricing system,[3] serves the widest territory – namely, every one of the forty-eight states. Even with this national distribution, a high percentage of the volume produced in these meal-producing states remains within their borders. In 1950 the following proportions of the soybean meal production remained in the

[3] The Decatur pricing system is discussed in the section on transportation in Chapter V.

Table 18. The Production and Distribution of Soybean Meal by States, 1945 [*]

State	Number of Thousand Tons			
	Production	Distribution	Surplus	Deficit
New York	139.0	422.5	......	283.5
Illinois	1,210.5	402.5	808.0	......
Ohio	435.0	347.5	87.5	......
Iowa	596.0	325.5	270.5	......
Indiana	450.0	244.0	206.0	......
Minnesota	105.5	225.5	......	120.0
Missouri	127.5	177.0	......	49.5
Texas	100.0	176.0	......	76.0
Pennsylvania	15.5	153.5	......	138.0
California	49.0	152.0	......	103.0
Nebraska	51.0	118.0	......	67.0
Tennessee	71.0	101.0	......	30.0
Wisconsin	19.5	99.0	......	79.5
Kansas	84.0	94.0	......	10.0
Michigan	13.0	58.0	......	45.0
Washington	......	52.0	......	52.0
Oklahoma	22.5	51.5	......	29.0
Kentucky	123.5	47.5	76.0	......
Vermont	......	44.5	......	44.5
North Carolina	20.0	42.5	......	22.5
Virginia	20.5	42.0	......	21.5
Colorado	......	35.5	......	35.5
Oregon	......	34.5	......	34.5
Georgia	30.5	34.0	......	3.5
Maryland	......	33.0	......	33.0
Alabama	25.5	33.5	......	8.0
Massachusetts	......	29.0	......	29.0
Delaware	1.5	28.5	......	27.0
New Jersey	......	24.5	......	24.5
Florida	3.0	23.0	......	20.0
Utah	......	20.0	......	20.0
South Dakota	11.0	15.0	......	4.0
Mississippi	17.0	14.5	2.5	......
Louisiana	9.0	14.0	......	5.0
Montana	......	14.0	......	14.0
Arkansas	69.5	13.5	56.0	......
Wyoming	......	10.0	......	10.0
New Mexico	......	9.0	......	9.0
Idaho	......	8.5	......	8.5
South Carolina	1.0	8.5	......	7.5
Connecticut	......	8.0	......	8.0
West Virginia	......	6.5	......	6.5
North Dakota	1.0	6.0	......	5.0
New Hampshire	......	6.0	......	6.0
Arizona	1.0	2.0	......	1.0
Maine	......	1.5	......	1.5
Rhode Island	......	1.0	......	1.0
Nevada	......	1.0	......	1.0
Total	3,823.0	3,810.5	1,506.5	1,494.0

[*] Source: P.M.A., U.S. Department of Agriculture.

respective producing states: Illinois 20 per cent, Indiana 10 per cent, Iowa 17 per cent, Ohio 9 per cent, Missouri 25 per cent, and Minnesota 61 per cent (Appendix, Table 13). These percentages indicate the strength of the local market of each of these states relative to the soybean meal produced there. Comparisons of these various percentages indicate that Minnesota processors have the best local meal market.

The United States is an excellent market for soybean meal and other high protein concentrates (Appendix, Table 14). The consumption of all high protein concentrates advanced from a prewar average of 7,500,000 tons to a consumption of 11,100,000 tons in 1949. Practically all of this expansion was accounted for by the increasing use of soybean meal (Appendix, Table 14, and Figure 16).

Three of the most important factors in this enlargement of the soybean meal market are, first, the fact that, as nutritional studies indicate, protein requirements for the most efficient growth of animals are not being met; second, the large increase in the livestock population, and third, the expansion of the mixed feed industry. Of course, the last two factors are dependent upon a full-employment economy, together with a good income-distribution, which permits an increase of meat in the diet.

The deficit in digestible protein for all livestock was ascertained by Mr. R. D. Jennings of the Bureau of Agricultural Economics on the basis of Morrison's *Feeds and Feeding* (Table 19). The deficit is expressed in terms of soybean meal equivalent; and for 1949 the deficit was 6,682,000 tons of soybean meal. In essence, this means that if most of the protein increase required were to come from soybean production

FIGURE 16. Production of Specified Protein Concentrates, United States, 1937–1949.

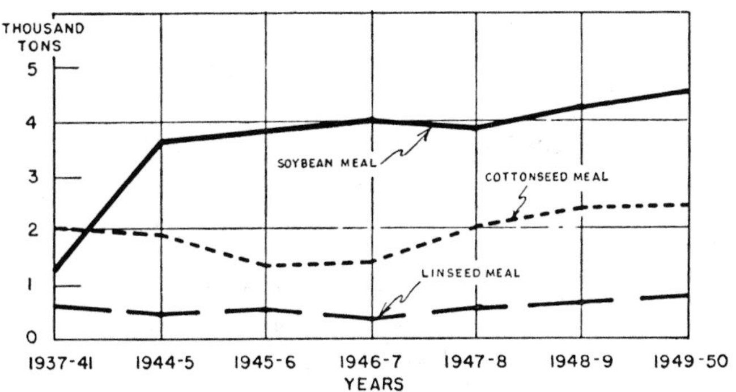

TABLE 19. The Deficit in Protein for All Livestock, Using Requirements Given in Feeding Standards as the Quantity Needed, 1937 through 1949 *

Feeding Year Beginning October 1	Number of Thousand Tons of Concentrates Fed †	Percentage of Digestible Protein Needed	Number of Thousand Tons			
			Total Digestible Protein Needed	Digestible Protein Fed	Deficit in Digestible Protein	Deficit Expressed in Soybean Meal
1937	95,090	11.56	10,992	9,825	1,167	3,334
1938	97,146	11.60	11,269	9,765	1,504	4,297
1939	100,418	11.60	11,648	10,036	1,612	4,606
1940	106,108	11.68	12,393	10,722	1,671	4,774
1941	116,408	11.72	13,643	11,610	2,033	5,808
1942	140,284	11.66	16,357	14,027	2,330	6,657
1943	136,995	11.75	16,097	13,827	2,270	6,485
1944	126,125	11.84	14,933	12,741	2,192	6,263
1945	130,427	11.79	15,377	12,841	2,536	7,246
1946	120,599	11.85	14,291	11,981	2,310	6,000
1947	108,245	11.89	12,870	11,117	1,753	5,008
1948	120,280	11.91	14,325	12,184	2,141	6,117
1949	124,693	11.90	14,838	12,499	2,339	6,682

* Source: R. D. Jennings, *op. cit.*, p. 2.
† All grain (excluding corn in silage) and by-product feeds, including seeds and skim milk fed.

alone, a crop of over 500 million bushels would be necessary. This protein deficit in the feeding of livestock is extremely important considering the high protein content of the products of livestock. On the average, beef contains 36 per cent protein, pork 27 per cent, chicken 60 per cent, eggs 49 per cent, and milk 27 per cent.[4] A ration that lacks sufficient protein proves to be inefficient when fed to livestock – it takes more pounds of grain to produce the same gain in weight if too little protein is fed. However, the price relation between the additional protein needed, the added grain consumed, and what the livestock bring on the market may be such as to make it unprofitable to try to feed as much protein as suggested by Morrison's feeding standards. At present, however, the protein deficiency is so great that at least some gain would seem feasible from the standpoint of both nutrition and profit.

FIGURE 17. Utilization of Soybean Oil Meal among Classes of Livestock: Percentage Distribution, United States, 1950.

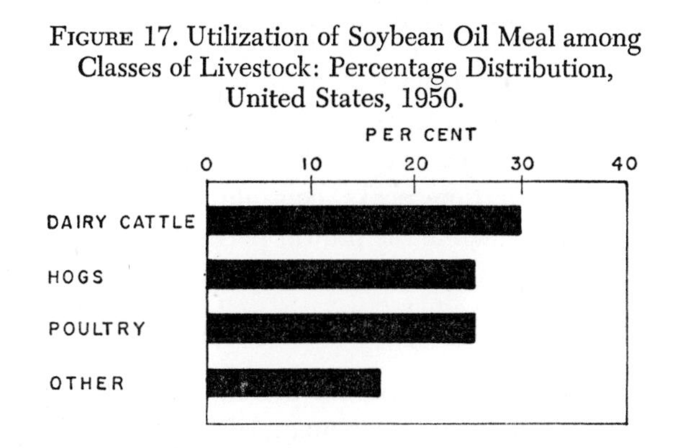

Coupled with this need for more protein in the ration is the unusual increase in our livestock population. Every type of livestock, with the exception of sheep, has made exceptional gains in the postwar period over the prewar average. At present there is no indication of any change in this expansion, with the exception of a slight decrease in the hog population. Not only has the per-animal unit of each of the types of livestock advanced, but in addition the livestock production per animal has increased. There is more milk per cow produced as well as eggs per chicken and weight per hog. All of these increases in the products of animals as well as in the number of animal units have meant additional demands for protein supplies (Figure 17).

[4] R. D. Jennings, *A Look at the Protein Situation for Livestock* (B.A.E., U.S. Department of Agriculture, March 1950).

Further expansion of protein supplies has also been brought about by the needs and experimentation of a growing mixed-feed industry. The Bureau of Census indicated in 1947 that the mixed-feed industry had twice as many manufacturing plants as it did in the prewar period; it produced one fifth of the total concentrates fed to livestock; and produced 1.7 times as many tons of feeds as it produced in the prewar period – or a total of 22 million tons. The census also reported that 70 to 75 per cent of all the soybean meal utilized went into mixed feeds; the corresponding figures for linseed meal and cottonseed meal are 40 to 50 per cent and 15 to 20 per cent respectively. In more recent years the mixed-feed industry has grown even more rapidly, a growth indicating an additional demand for soybean meal. Of course, the real impetus for the expansion of the soybean-meal market in the United States has come from a full-employment economy and a more equitable distribution of incomes. The per-capita income in this country has increased over 150 per cent from 1940 to 1950. At the same time the per-capita consumption of meat has risen sharply, as families are in a better position to buy more meat. Even with the drop in meat consumption per capita from the wartime peaks, consumption is about ten pounds higher per capita now than in the prewar period. Moreover, the population of the United States has increased rapidly during the last decade, to expand further the market for meat and, in turn, the market for soybean meal.

The sources of supply available for this intense protein demand are principally four in number: (1) commercial high protein feeds, which supply about 10 per cent of the total protein consumed, and of which oil meals comprise about three fourths of the tonnage;[5] (2) grains such as corn and oats, which supply from 20 to 25 per cent of the total; (3) hay and silage, which supply about 26 per cent; and (4) pastures, about 35 per cent.

The soybean producer and processor are most interested in the commercial high-protein feeds, but all of these sources of supply affect one another.

The four main protein feed sources can expand their supplies in several ways. Increases in the supply of hay and pasture protein can be brought about by better farming practices and timely cutting of the hay crop. Increasing the protein value of hybrid corn is more difficult. Open-pollinated varieties of corn contain approximately 7 per cent pro-

[5] *Ibid.*

tein, whereas hybrid corn contains about 6.5 per cent protein. The significance of this protein variation is very important, for approximately 1 million additional tons of soybean meal is needed to supplement the average hybrid corn crop. A more encouraging development is the discovery of the animal-protein factor which enables plant protein to be substituted for the higher-priced animal proteins.

On the whole, increases in the protein supplies mentioned above do not seem to be occurring rapidly. Hence, in the expansion of production, soybean meal is primarily in competition with the other commercial protein oil meals – namely, linseed and cottonseed.

The standard specifications for soybean oil meal in the *1950–1951 Year Book and Trading Rules* of the National Soybean Processors Association were as follows:

"Soybean chips, soybean oil cake, and 41 per cent protein soybean oil meal are produced by cooking ground soybeans and reducing the oil content of the cooked product by pressure to 5 per cent or less on a commercial basis. Standard specifications are as follows:

Protein	Minimum	41.0%
Fat	Minimum	3.5%
Fibre	Maximum	7.0%
N.F.E.	Minimum	27.0%
Moisture (when shipped by seller)	Maximum	12.0%

Soybean flakes and 44 per cent protein soybean oil meal are produced by conditioning ground soybeans and reducing the oil content of the conditioned product by the use of solvents to 1 per cent or less on a commercial basis. Standard specifications are as follows:

Protein	Minimum	44.0%
Fat	Minimum	0.5%
Fibre	Maximum	7.0%
N.F.E.	Minimum	27.0%
Moisture (when shipped by seller)	Maximum	12.0%"

The minimum protein requirement for cottonseed meal is 41 per cent and for linseed meal 33 per cent and 36 per cent, depending upon the manufacturing process used. The variation in the protein composition of these main competing oil meals is more clearly demonstrated by the breakdown and analysis of their respective amino acids.[6]

The similarity in protein content of soybean meal and cottonseed

[6] Protein is a complex substance made up of more than twenty amino acids, which repair and build body tissues and help in the production of eggs and milk. Some of these acids are manufactured in the body, but others have to be supplied by the feed.

FIGURE 18. Prices of Soybean, Cottonseed, and Linseed Oil Meals, 1940–1950.

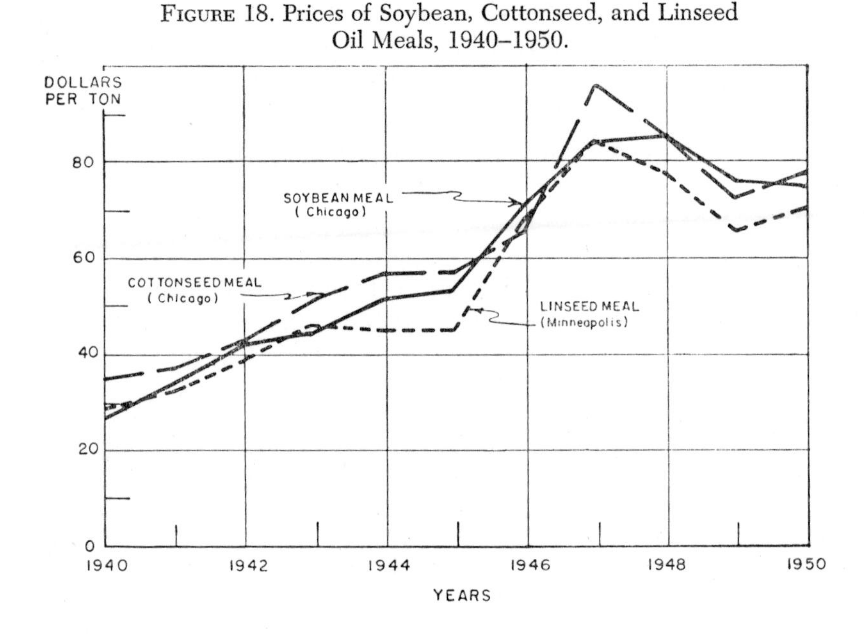

meal has led to a close price relationship (Fig. 18). However, there are limits to the substitutability of these two meals that cause wider differences than those indicated by Figure 18. For example, the use of cottonseed meal is not advisable for chickens which produce eggs for storage, as the yolks will yellow over time. Other factors causing a variation in price between cottonseed meal and soybean meal are the different movements of the crops and meals and the seasonal requirements of the various types of livestock. Table 20 illustrates the seasonal price swings of the two meals. The 1950 average price of soybean meal per 100 pounds was 30 cents above the price of cottonseed meal; yet, in October through December of that year, cottonseed meal was higher in price than soybean meal.

The price of linseed meal is also competitive with the price of soybean meal and cottonseed meal; but, because of linseed meal's slightly smaller protein content, it is usually lower in price than the other two meals (Fig. 18).

In spite of these minor differences in protein content and in use, as well as these seasonal limitations, a high coefficient of determination does exist between the price of soybean meal and the price of other

TABLE 20. Prices Paid by Farmers per 100 Pounds of Cottonseed Meal and Soybean Meal, by Months, United States, 1950 *

Month	Cottonseed Meal	Soybean Meal
January 15	$3.84	$4.20
February 15	3.76	4.02
March 15	3.74	4.11
April 15	3.85	4.19
May 15	3.97	4.58
June 15	4.00	4.73
July 15	4.10	5.16
August 15	4.48	5.01
September 15	4.35	4.44
October 15	4.34	4.15
November 15	4.42	4.24
December 15	4.67	4.34
Average	$4.13	$4.43

* Source: *Feed Statistics,* December 1950 (B.A.E., U.S. Department of Agriculture, Technical Bulletin No. 95), p. 46.

high-protein feeds (Appendix, Table 15). The year-to-year changes indicate less relation than do the long-run averages (Appendix, Table 15). Moreover, seasonal changes are lost in the examination of calendar-year changes. Competition among these feeds is intensive for particular markets, and this fact, together with the over-all demand for all protein feeds, would tend to result in relatively high correlations between prices of soybean meal and prices of other high-protein feeds.

A weighty factor, and one that will probably prove to be decisive, in the long-run development of soybean meal is that soybean meal in 1951 became the most important product of the soybean not only in quantity (80 per cent) but also in monetary value (62 per cent). By contrast, linseed meal is a fairly minor product of flax, representing 60 per cent in quantity and only 23 per cent in monetary value. Cotton fiber also is a much more important product of the cotton crop than cottonseed meal. The increased production of cottonseed meal and linseed meal, therefore, is dependent upon the demand for cotton fiber and linseed oil. Consequently soybean meal is in the best position to meet directly the real and potential demand for high protein feeds.

Soybean meal production, however, cannot be isolated entirely from the demands of soybean oil. In the early months of 1952 the price of soybean oil dropped sharply, but the price of soybeans stayed up; as a result the crushing margin (the difference between the price of meal and oil and the price of soybeans) fell below the processing costs of many firms. Many small firms had to cease operations or produce inferior products.[7] These fluctuating crushing margins caused by changing price relations between soybeans and meal and oil result in variations in soybean meal production. Hence, despite the importance of meal as the main product of the soybean, soybean oil does act as a restraining or contributing influence upon the contraction or expansion of the production of soybean meal.

In spite of the enormous deficit in protein feeds and the increasing livestock population, the price index of oilseed meals from 1945 to 1950 exceeded the index for livestock and livestock products in only one year. This indicates the excellent response of producers and processors in expanding the production of soybean meal. However, it also indicates that meal must be relatively cheap to induce more farmers to use soybean meal. During the wartime period oil was the most important monetary by-product of the soybean, and supplies of meal had to be moved at low levels in relation to the price of corn and other feeds. Today (March 1952) the situation is reversed: meal is the dominant monetary product of the soybean, and oil has to be sold at low price levels in order to be moved.

The use of soybean meal or flakes for direct human consumption is minute, as over 90 per cent of the meal is utilized in livestock feeding. The products used in human consumption are principally soya flour and soya grits. Soya flour is not a substitute for wheat flour, but is used to enrich baking products and other foods. Nutritionists stress its food value, but as the presence of soya flour is noticeable in the taste and color of the bread, there has been some consumer resistance. Soya grits were promoted during the war as meat-extenders. Once the palatability of soya flour and grits is improved, the direct human consumption of these products will probably increase.

The use of soybean meal and soybean proteins in the industrial market is also slight. A recent study, completed in September 1951, indicates that the present and potential industrial market for soybean vegetable proteins will remain unimportant when compared to the

[7] This point will be discussed more fully in Chapter V.

practically unlimited demand for soybean meal in livestock feeding.[8]

In summary, full employment, good income-distribution, and other motivations, rational, psychological, and irrational, have increased the per-capita consumption of meat in the United States. The government's encouragment of the expansion of the livestock population during the war years, together with the market demand, caused the livestock population to reach a new figure. The studies of animal nutritionists and the experimental work of the mixed-feed industry have increased the demands for protein supplies even further. At the same time the expansion of the soybean crop in this country enabled soybean meal to provide over 90 per cent of the increase in the supply of all high-protein feeds.

This dominance of soybean meal as the chief supplier of high-protein feed will probably continue in the future, as the demands for soybean meal can be met more directly by the soybean producer and processor than by the processor of the by-products of cotton and linseed oil. However, the market for all of these high-protein meals will shrink if a change in the over-all economic situation should lower the demand for meat. If this should come to be the case, the farmer would look to his home-grown feeds, hay, and pasture for his source of protein rather than to soybean meal or the other oil meals. The market for soybean meal in Minnesota will probably remain relatively good, even if demand for meat falls off, because so much of the Minnesota soybean meal production is consumed within the state.

Finally, the production of soybean meal cannot be separated entirely from the market demand for soybean oil, as both enter into the processors' manufacturing decisions.

SOYBEAN OIL UTILIZATION

The expansion of the soybean crop and the processing industry has led to an increased production of soybean oil in the United States (Appendix, Table 16). Until 1951, soybean oil was the most valuable monetary product of the soybean. Although there are many diverse markets for soybean oil, essentially there are three main uses of this product, namely, shortening, margarine, and salad oils (Fig. 19). Since over 80 per cent of soybean oil is consumed by human beings, most of the

[8] *Marketing Potential for Oilseed Protein Materials in Industrial Uses* (B.A.E., U.S. Department of Agriculture, Technical Bulletin No. 1043, September 1951).

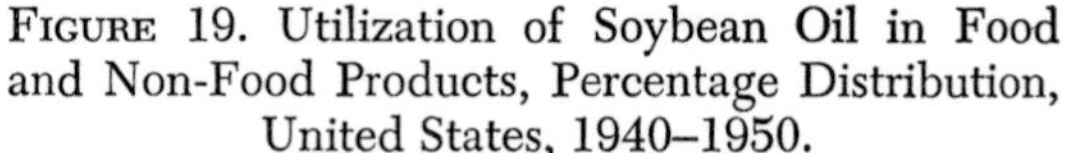

FIGURE 19. Utilization of Soybean Oil in Food and Non-Food Products, Percentage Distribution, United States, 1940–1950.

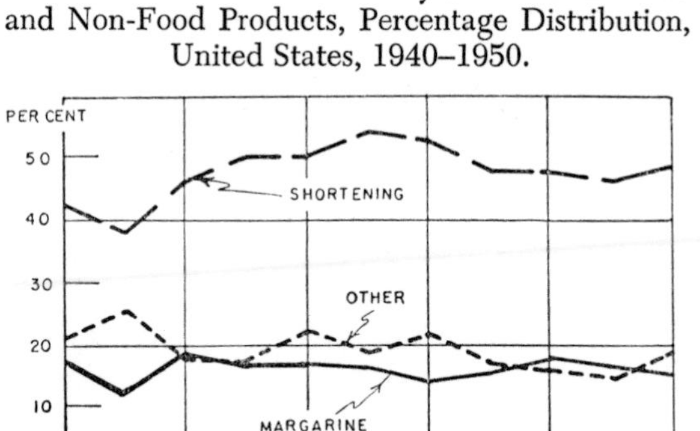

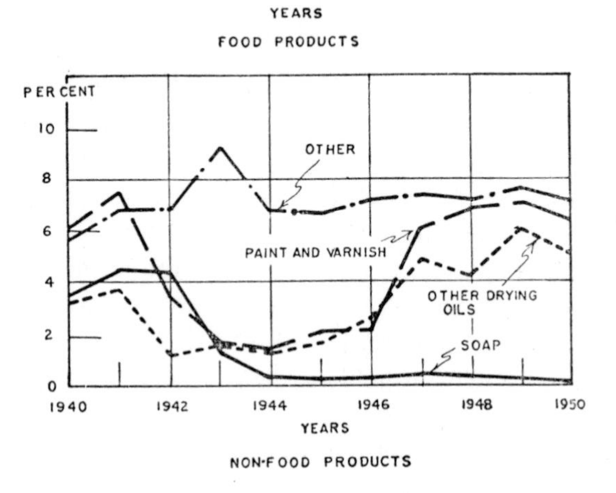

expansion in its production has taken place at the expense of other fats and oils formerly consumed by the public. The supply of soybean oil, measured as a percentage of all fats and oils except butter and lard produced in the United States, has risen rapidly, reaching a high of 37 per cent in 1949. On the other hand, the supply of cottonseed oil (measured on the same basis), its chief competitor, has declined steadily (Figs. 20 and 21).

The consumption of soybean oil in the United States was stimulated by World War II and the resultant loss of imports of edible oils. Other factors stimulating consumption are the versatility of soybean oil, its favorable price, tariff protection, and the aggressiveness of soybean producers and processors in finding new uses for the oil.

FIGURE 20. Supply of Cottonseed, Soybean, Coconut, and Other Oils and Food Fats, Not Including Butter and Lard: Percentage Distribution, United States, 1920–1949.

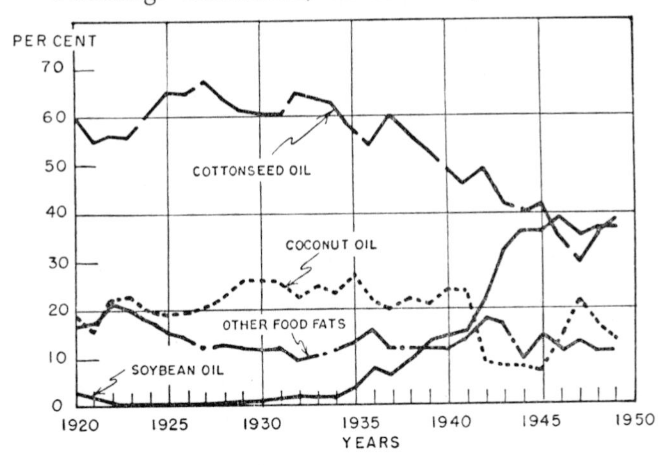

FIGURE 21. Supply of Food Fats and Oils, United States, 1920–1949.

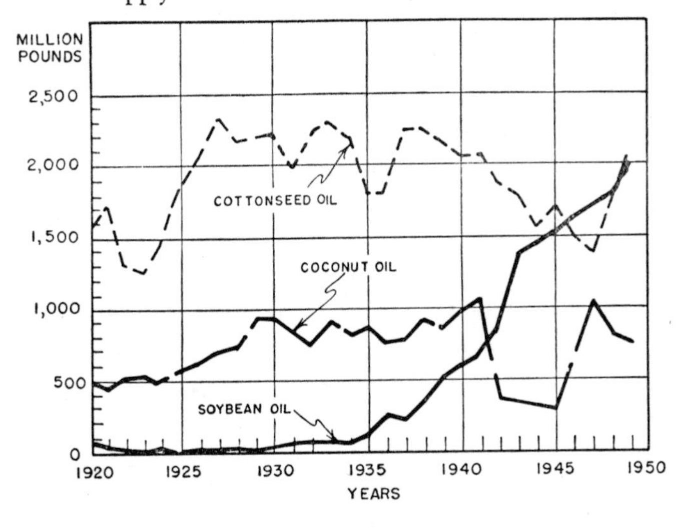

Other conditions brought about major changes in the utilization of fats and oils in different products in the United States. In the mid-1930's many state laws were passed taxing margarine containing *non-domestic* fats and oils more heavily than domestic margarine. The chief non-domestic ingredient of margarine was coconut oil. To replace this ingredient, cottonseed oil was more rapidly adopted than soybean oil because of the tendency of the latter to flavor reversion. Nevertheless, the proportion of soybean oil used in margarine increased to 40 per cent in 1950, reaching highs of 42 per cent during the war. The use of soybean oil in shortening also increased, and that of cottonseed declined.

The specifications for buying and selling soybean oil for technical uses and an analysis of the fatty acids soybean oil contains indicate the limitations and possibilities it has commercially. Because of its low iodine number and its high percentage of linoleic acid, it is not preferred in the drying-oil industries. On the other hand, it does not yellow over time, and this, in part, makes up for its slow-drying qualities. In addition to this limitation for industrial use, it is not considered the most satisfactory oil for edible use, where its tendency toward flavor reversion is its chief disadvantage. The Regional Soybean Laboratory at Peoria has cooperated with industry on both these major problems in the utilization of soybean oil and has achieved outstanding results. Flavor reversion has been lessened, and the developments in hydrogenation[9] have widened the use of soybean oil in the edible market. Technical investigation directed toward the greater utilization of soybean oil in the industrial market has centered in research in molecular fractional distillation.[10] These research efforts have changed soybean oil from an edible and drying oil of medium quality into an excellent usable product in both markets.

World and national trade movements. From an earlier consideration of the international market (Chapter II) it is evident that much of our soybean oil has been going into foreign trade, especially to Western Europe. Approximately 20 per cent of the domestic soybean oil crop was exported in 1949. The world market is important not only for soybean oil as such but also for other, competing domestic fats and oils. For example, lard competes with vegetable shortening, which contains large quantities of soybean oil. In 1950 over 5,000 tank cars of soybean oil were exported to Europe.[11] In the same year the United States exported over 8,000 tank cars of lard. If the foreign market can acquire

[9] A process whereby hydrogen is added to the oil to solidify it at room temperatures, as in products like Crisco and Spry.

[10] The process of splitting oils into their fatty acids and glycerines and recombining the best qualities for certain chemical and physical properties.

[11] A tank car is 60,000 pounds.

cheaper edible fats and oils, such as olive oil, then soybean oil will not only lose its foreign market but will also have to compete with a larger and cheaper domestic supply of lard. The importance of the world market for all fats and oils is emphasized by the fact that in 1938 (taking into account lard, soybean oil, coconut oil, and cottonseed oil) the United States was a net importer of 8,000 tanks, whereas in 1950, it was a net exporter of 3,500 tanks.[12] The chief markets for soybean oil are located in the refining and population centers of the East Coast, the West Coast, and the South (Appendix, Table 17, and Fig. 22). Unlike

FIGURE 22. Location of Principal Producers of Shortening, Margarine, Salad and Cooking Oils, United States, June 1945.

for soybean meal, the principal consuming areas for oil are normally not found in the prominent processing states. (This fact is of special importance in analyzing processing plant location in Chapter V.)

Price relations. Soybean oil competes directly with cottonseed oil and indirectly with lard and butter in the domestic edible oil market (Fig. 23). In addition, it is somewhat competitive to linseed oil in the drying oil market. The limiting factor in all of these various competitions is the cost of breaking down soybean oil into the chemical properties suited

[12] Ralph G. Golseth, *Trading in Fats and Oils* (Commodity Markets Symposium, Chicago, September 6, 1951).

FIGURE 23. Supply of Butter, Lard, and Other Major Food Fats and Oils: Percentage Distribution, United States, 1920–1950.

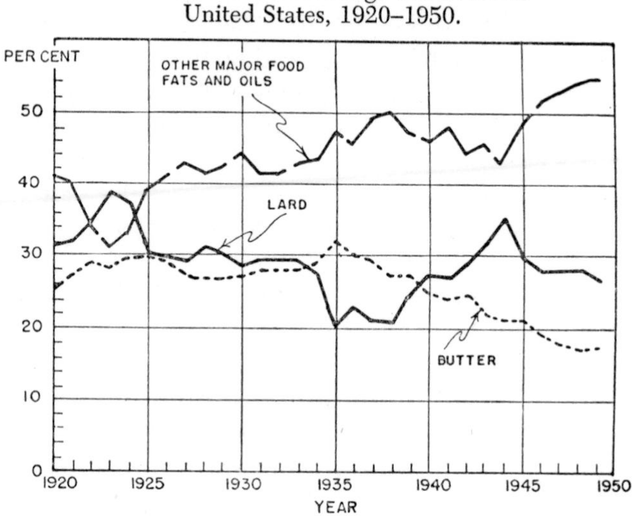

FIGURE 24. Wholesale Prices of Cottonseed Oil and Soybean Oil, United States, 1935–1949.

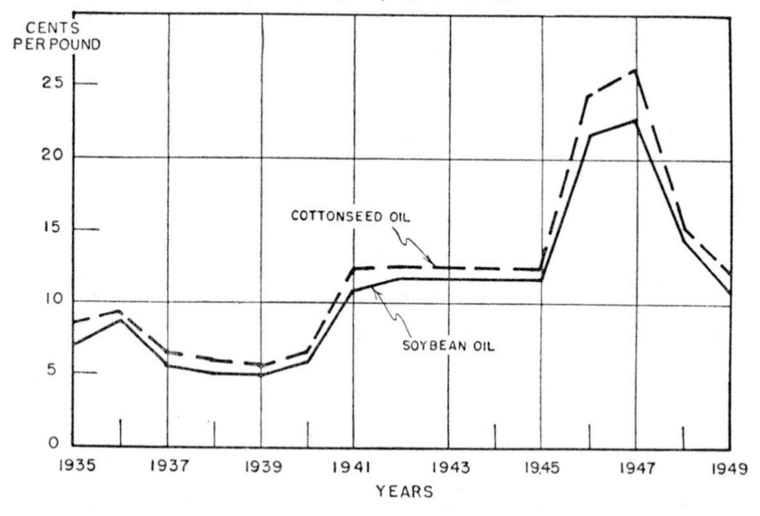

for each particular use and the cost of changing the formula of the end product. In price cottonseed oil and soybean oil are fairly close (Fig. 24). Their average relation indicates an approximately 1-cent premium for cottonseed oil. This difference is probably due to the tendency toward flavor reversion of soybean oil in margarine. Wider fluctuations exist between the prices of linseed oil and soybean oil. The differential averages around 3 cents a pound and ranges from 2 to 11 cents (Appendix, Table 18). There is a basic minimum of oil of fast-drying quality needed in paint; therefore, linseed oil will probably remain the dominant oil in this market despite price relations favorable to soybean oil. To understand the complex competition that exists in the principal product-uses of soybean oil, a separate examination of each is required.

Shortening. The most important vegetable oil product is shortening. Over 47 per cent of the domestic disappearance of soybean oil, 28 per cent of cottonseed oil, and 23 per cent of peanut oil go into shortening. Approximately 1,311 million pounds of shortening was consumed in 1950. The proportion of soybean oil used in shortening in 1950 was 49 per cent of the total oils utilized (Fig. 25). Hence, the relation of vegetable shortening to its competitors does affect the demand for soybean oil.

The chief competitor of vegetable shortening is lard. Before World War II, tank-car lots of lard were selling at slightly more than 1 cent a pound above soybean oil (Appendix, Table 19). At the present time soybean oil is selling at from 1 to 3 cents above lard, a differential in-

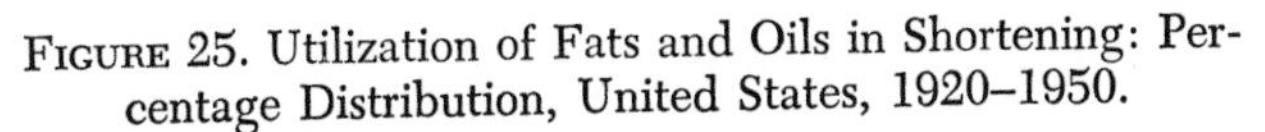
FIGURE 25. Utilization of Fats and Oils in Shortening: Percentage Distribution, United States, 1920–1950.

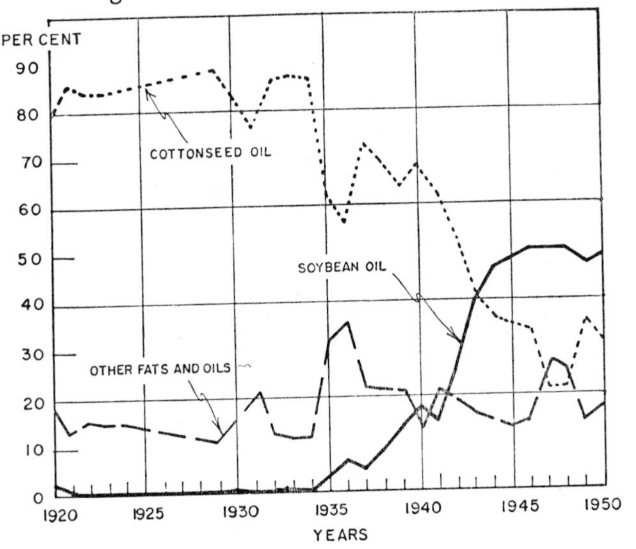

dicating the strong consumer preference that has developed for vegetable shortening. This price differential is even larger in view of the fact that it costs a great deal more to produce a pound of vegetable shortening from crude vegetable oils than it does to produce a pound of marketable lard from loose lard. The uniform quality of vegetable shortenings has also added to consumer preference. Unlike the household trade, industrial users (such as bakers) switch back and forth between vegetable shortening and lard, depending upon the market price.

It seems likely that the large proportion of soybean oil used in shortening will continue. The demand for soybean meal induces high levels of processing production. Oil, being in surplus, continues to glut the market at extremely low and favorable consumption prices.

Margarine. The next important product containing a large proportion of soybean oil is margarine. In the prewar years soybean oil accounted for 21 per cent of all the fats and oils used in margarine; and cottonseed oil, 47 per cent. At the present time the corresponding figures are 40 and 56 per cent respectively. In more recent months a greater tonnage of soybean oil than of cottonseed oil has been used in the production of margarine. Cottonseed oil has a slight advantage in reversion-quality, but soybean oil technology is rapidly overcoming this problem, as indicated by the small price differential between the two oils.[13]

The chief competitor of margarine is butter. Margarine consumption has been of growing importance in the United States from 1912 to the present time. In 1951 the consumption of margarine in the United States was more than 6.5 pounds per capita, or over 1 billion pounds. A recent stimulus to this development was the repeal of the federal tax on colored margarine, which became effective July 1, 1950. The war and postwar shortage of butter was also an important factor in the rapid increase in margarine consumption. The reduction in butter supplies during the war reduced butter consumption, which has since not recovered its former level. The price ratio between butter and margarine has remained fairly constant at 2.2. With the recent sharp decrease in the price of vegetable oils and the relaxing of state margarine tax laws, the ratio of butter prices to margarine prices may be larger.[14] The price of butter will probably not decline to any noticeable extent

[13] In the short cottonseed-oil crop-year of 1950, the demand for cottonseed oil was unusual, and a much higher price differential between soybean and cottonseed oil existed than the 0.3-cent differential for 1949.

[14] State taxes and license fees for margarine still exist in seven states.

because of the high wholesale support-price of butter at 66 cents a pound. With the possibility of a higher price-ratio between butter and margarine, margarine consumption will increase even more and prove to be an expanding outlet for soybean oil.

Other edible uses. Other edible markets for soybean oil include salad oils, cooking oils, salad dressings, and mayonnaise. These products take about 18.3 per cent of the total disappearance of soybean oil, 33 per cent of cottonseed oil, and 90 per cent of corn oil. Of the constituents of these salad oils and cooking oils, soybean oil accounts for approximately 25 per cent of the total, cottonseed oil 40 per cent, and corn oil 18 per cent. The competition among these vegetable oils when used for cooking is primarily based upon flavor formulas that have been used in the past. Although some manufacturers will add animal fat for cooking purposes when price differentials are wide enough, most manufacturers confine themselves to vegetable oils in their cooking. Many company policies and guarantees on the final product specify "the use of vegetable cooking oils only," competition thus being limited to one vegetable oil against another. The increasing use of soybean oil in this market demonstrates that, up to a certain maximum, its flavor is suitable. Up to this maximum formula point, price is the factor which determines the use or non-use of soybean oil.

In the words of Dr. Rex W. Cox, "In the range within which fats and oils have properties in common and are substitutable in the manufacture of a specified product, competition is intensive, the demand for the individual item is elastic, and, therefore, the extent of its use is determined largely by the price relative to the prices of competing fats and oils. When a fat or oil has peculiar properties which make it especially suitable in a specified use, competition of the item with others is subordinate, and, in consequence, the demand of it is likely to be inelastic." [15]

Industrial uses. Even with the advent of molecular fractional distillation, the proportion of soybean oil used in the manufacture of paints, varnishes, linoleum, etc., is very small. In the paint market, soybean oil does have the advantages of not yellowing as easily as linseed oil. But its low drying-quality has to be overcome by adding fast-drying oils such as tung and oiticica to the paint formulas. Paint and varnish

[15] *Minnesota Farmer's Interest in Fats and Oil-Bearing Products* (Agricultural Experiment Station Bulletin No. 376, University of Minnesota, June 1944).

products comprise the most important industrial outlets for soybean oil, accounting for 15 per cent of its total domestic disappearance. New technology may enlarge this industrial market. But the wide price-differential of 7 cents a pound between linseed oil and soybean oil (January 1952) indicates that soybean-oil consumption is limited to small quantities by the paint industry.

In summary, the supply and consumption of soybean oil in the United States have increased enormously. Soybean oil has accounted for an increasing proportion of the oils used in shortening and margarine. At the same time, shortening and margarine consumption has risen, the result being an expanded vegetable-oil market.

Like the production of soybean meal, soybean-oil production has been expanded more than that of its main competitor, cottonseed oil. This has occurred because, dollarwise, soybean oil is more important to the soybean producer than cottonseed oil is to the cotton producer. Cotton production is much more dependent upon the demands for cotton fiber. Volumewise, the ratio of soybean meal to soybean oil in the processing process is 4.5 to 1. During the war and immediate postwar period the monetary ratio of soybean oil to meal exceeded the quantity ratio of soybean meal to oil, a circumstance indicating the dollar-and-cents importance of soybean oil to the processor and producer of soybeans. In recent years the monetary ratio of soybean oil to meal has fallen below the quantity ratio of soybean meal to oil; thus soybean oil is not now the most valuable product of the soybean in either a monetary or physical sense. The historical price ratio of soybean oil to meal is as follows:

Year	Ratio	Year	Ratio
1932	3.4	1948	4.8
1937	4.1	1949	3.8
1942	5.5	1950	3.7
1947	5.7	1951	3.0

The drop in the price of soybean oil in 1951 was due to the large world-supply of edible oils, the 75 per cent increase in the cotton crop in the United States, and the lesser E.C.A. funds used for the purchase of oil in this country.

In spite of the expanding margarine and shortening market and the increased technological development of soybean oil, the pressure of large world edible-oil supplies, coupled with the limitations of soybean oil in flavor and iodine content, will mean continued low prices for soybean oil. If world potential demand for fats and oils becomes an effective demand through additional E.C.A. funds or stronger foreign economies, and if technology continues to enlarge the uses of soybean oil, then soybean oil will not be relegated to its secondary position as a product of the soybean.

MINNESOTA UTILIZATION

Having analyzed the world and national markets for soybeans and soybean products, we may now examine the Minnesota market for these same products within the framework of the preceding analysis.

The large exports of soybeans and soybean oil from this country have had a direct impact upon the utilization of Minnesota soybeans. Over 20 per cent of the Minnesota soybean crop in 1951 went into the foreign market – primarily to Canada and Japan. The proximity of Minnesota to Canada makes trade with that country feasible. On the other hand, transportation costs involved in the shipment of soybeans to Japan present a special problem that will be discussed in Chapter V.

TABLE 21. The Production and Processing of Soybeans in Minnesota, Iowa, and Illinois

Year	Number of Thousand Bushels of Soybeans Crushed			Number of Thousand Bushels of Soybeans Produced		
	Minn.	Iowa	Ill.	Minn.	Iowa	Ill.
1945*	2,400	29,300	59,500	6,500	35,300	75,200‡
1949†	7,200	34,400	73,500	12,300	30,800	85,462
1950	7,100	39,950	73,800	16,400	42,300	94,752
1951§	9,800	38,200	101,700	18,300**	32,300	88,300

* *Soybean Digest*, 1945.
† Bureau of the Census, *Facts for Industry*.
‡ *Soybean Blue Book*.
§ Based on production figure through October 31, 1951.
** *Soybean Digest*, November 1951, p. 31.

The main outlet for Minnesota soybean production is the Minnesota processing industry, which consumes approximately 60 per cent of the crop (Table 21). The demand for soybean meal in Minnesota is excellent, just as it is on the national level, a situation encouraging the expansion of the Minnesota processing industry.[16] The market outlet for

[16] The development of the processing industry and its location will be discussed in Chapters IV and V.

TABLE 22. Minnesota Monthly Production of Soybean Meal, October 1950 through September 1951, and Monthly Consumption of Soybean Meal, October 1945 through September 1946 *

Month	Production, Tons	Consumption, Tons
October	15,285	16,721
November	15,688	21,905
December	22,336	21,522
January	20,419	20,906
February	20,970	18,583
March	22,596	23,065
April	15,805	20,587
May	19,230	27,976
June	19,446	18,522
July	19,008	15,577
August	20,139	12,915
September	17,186	12,095
Total	226,104	230,074

* These are the latest actual state consumption figures available and were obtained when all processing was under government contracts.

soybean meal in Minnesota is greater than the meal production within the state (Table 22). The factors bringing about this excellent demand for soybean meal in Minnesota are exactly the same as those expressed in the analysis of the national soybean-meal market. The increasing Minnesota livestock population, especially the increasing numbers of hogs and chickens, has expanded the demand for soybean meal. The decreases in hay and pasture acreage, which have resulted in fewer protein supplies, have further increased this demand.

The next important markets for the Minnesota soybean crop are other soybean-processing states. For example, northern Iowa processors rely on the soybean production of southern Minnesota for much of their soybean supplies. On the average, Iowa receives one fourth of all the soybean railroad shipments originating in Minnesota (Appendix, Table 20). If northern Iowa is considered together with southern Minnesota as one production and processing unit, then Minnesota could not be regarded as a surplus soybean state.

The market for crude soybean oil within the state is negligible because of the lack of refineries in Minnesota (Fig. 22). The low price of oil, together with disadvantages in oil transportation and location, counteracts much of the strong state market for meal.

SUMMARY

In summary, this chapter has analyzed the utilization of soybeans and soybean products at world, national, and state levels. The potential world demand for the chief products of the soybean – meal and oil – is unlimited. Effective foreign demand, on the other hand, has been dependent upon gifts and loans from the United States.

The national soybean meal market, potentially, could support the production of a 500-million-bushel soybean crop in order to meet the protein deficit in livestock feeding. Actual demand for meal in the United States has kept the price of soybean meal at the ceiling for the last half year (March 1952).[17]

The oil market has been extremely weak because of the increased production of other vegetable oils in the United States and the increased world supply of edible oils. Products containing large amounts of soybean oil, such as margarine and shortening, are being consumed in greater amounts. But neither this factor nor technological research in other uses for soybean oil has resulted in any strengthening of the oil market.

The Minnesota soybean and soybean-product market reflects the world and national situation. The strength of the state meal market has encouraged processing plant capacity, which growth, in turn, has meant an improved local outlet for Minnesota soybean production. The remaining soybean production goes to neighboring processing states and into the export market.

Historically, both the markets for soybean meal and oil in this country were vigorous enough to encourage the rapid expansion of the soybean crop. At the present time the robust meal market and the rather weak oil market partially offset one another, neither encouraging nor discouraging the expansion of the soybean crop. In order to ascertain the competitive position of the Minnesota soybean producer and processor in the context of present production and utilization, other factors affecting them must be analyzed. They include the development of the processing industry in the United States and in Minnesota, together with such things as commodity markets, storage, transportation, and price formulation, as these determine the advantages and disadvantages of the Minnesota location for producing and processing soybeans.

[17] Methods of avoiding the ceiling price have been attempted and will be discussed in Chapter V.

CHAPTER IV

The Processing Industry

BEFORE an analysis of the development of the processing industry is undertaken, it is essential to study the movement of the crop to the processor.

MARKETING CHANNELS OF THE CROP

A study of the marketing channels of the soybean crop in Illinois for 1947 and 1948 was published in October 1950 by the United States Department of Agriculture.[1] The Minnesota marketing movement is very similar to that of Illinois. Country elevators are of primary importance in the original purchase of the crop from the farmer, 96 per cent of it being handled by them in Illinois (Table 23). The processors in Minnesota estimate that country elevators in this state handled 90 per cent of the farmer's soybean crop, the remaining 10 per cent being bought directly by the processor.

The over-all gross saving of a small processing plant in obtaining its soybean supplies directly from the farmer is approximately 9.9 cents a bushel, as ascertained by the Illinois study (Table 24). This saving is obtained by avoiding the cost of the various marketing channels. However, the large processor who attempts to purchase his soybeans directly will probably find it more costly to canvass wide areas of production than to pay the service cost of specialized marketing groups. The large processor needs a tremendous amount of soybeans each day to run his plant at maximum capacity to achieve a low per-unit cost of production. This low processing cost per unit achieved in large-scale

[1] A. R. Sabin, *Marketing Channels and Margins for Soybeans and Soybean Products in Illinois* (B.A.E., U.S. Department of Agriculture, October 1950). Pages 14 and 6 of this work are the source of the data tabulated in Tables 23 and 24.

TABLE 23. Marketing Channels for Soybeans, Illinois, 1947–1948 Crop Years, as a Percentage of Total Sales off Farms

	Seller				
Buyer	Farms	Country Elevators	Interior Dealers	Commission Companies	Merchandisers
Country elevators	96	..	..	..	..
Interior dealers	..	53	..	..	..
Commission companies	..	21	..	..	..
Merchandisers	..	4	10	5	..
Processors	4	18	41	14	10
Out-of-state destinations	..	..	2	2	9
Total	100	96	53	21	19

TABLE 24. The Relative Costs of Acquiring Soybeans for Large and Small Processing Plants, Illinois, Crop Year 1948

	Cents per Bushel		
Item	Plants Crushing Over 1 Million Bushels per Year	Plants Crushing 1 Million Bushels and Under per Year	Average of All Plants
Cost over track, country station price*	4.4	−3.8	3.9
Outside storage, average for all beans processed	1.9	1.0	1.8
Insurance on beans stored outside	0.2	0.1	0.2
Net freight-in	2.2	1.5	2.2
Total (net cost over track, country station price)	8.7	−1.2	8.1

* Soybeans are sold by country elevators in carload lots on track at the elevator. The price is called "track, country station price" at that elevator site. The minus signs indicate that the prices paid by the processor to the farmer are under the country elevator track station price.

soybean processing plants more than offsets the advantage the small processing plant has in purchasing beans directly from the farmer.[2]

The state-to-state movement of soybeans from the six main soybean-producing states of Illinois, Indiana, Iowa, Minnesota, Missouri, and Ohio indicates a growing utilization of the crop within these producing states (Appendix, Table 20). Illinois, Iowa, and Ohio are primarily "deficit" states in the sense that the capacity of the soybean-processing

[2] This is evident by the unusual trend to large capacity soybean processing plants which will be discussed more fully in a later section of this chapter.

plants exceeds the production of the soybean crop in these states. The increase of processing capacity in the "surplus" soybean-producing state of Minnesota is evidenced by the rapid rise in the percentage of soybean shipments remaining within the state and the decline in the number of shipments out of the state.

The movement of the soybean crop from the producer to the processor having been examined, the next logical step is an analysis of the historical, technical, and economic development of the processing industry.

HISTORICAL EVOLUTION

THE NATIONAL PROCESSING INDUSTRY

Soybean processing in the United States began in 1910 when imported Manchurian soybeans were first crushed by an oil mill on the Pacific Coast.[3] In 1915 the first crushing of an American soybean crop occurred at Elizabeth City, North Carolina. In 1920 an expeller-type mill was used in processing soybean oil and meal from American-grown soybeans at Chicago Heights, Illinois. Large-scale production of oil and meal began in 1922 at Decatur, Illinois, under the leadership of the A. E. Staley Manufacturing Company. A year later the first solvent plant was built at Monticello, Illinois. In this embryo stage of the soybean processing industry, several other companies built soybean manufacturing plants – the Funk Brothers Seed Company in 1924, the Wm. O. Goodrich Company in 1926, the American Milling Company in 1927, the Shellabarger Grain Company and Archer-Daniels-Midland Company in 1929, the Central Soya Company in 1934, and the Spencer Kellogg Company in 1935.

By 1940 the soybean-processing industry was crushing 64 million bushels; by 1945, 153 million bushels; and by 1950, 222 million bushels. The processing capacity was not only large enough to crush the expanding soybean crop but it soon exceeded the available soybean supplies. In 1945 the capacity of processing plants, primarily used for soybeans, was 190 million bushels; and in 1950, 315 million bushels. If cottonseed processing mills were to decide to crush soybeans on a part-time basis, the soybean-processing capacity of the United States would be increased approximately 20 per cent.[4] The soybean-processing industry's

[3] Lamar Kishlar, in *Soybean Digest*, July 1941, p. 11.

[4] The cottonseed mills are primarily hydraulic operations that have been fully depreciated for several years; thus costs of production are low. In addition, more

overcapacity has led to intensive competition among the processors for the available soybean crop, and has meant excellent markets for soybean producers. This competition has encouraged the development of concerns with lower per-unit costs of production and newer types of processes.[5]

Several economic tendencies have been evident in the historical development of the processing industry in the United States that are equally significant in the industry's growth in Minnesota. One such tendency is that of vertical integration. Much of the expansion of the processing industry came about because of the need for soybean meal by mixed-feed producers. In order to be certain of a supply of meal at a fairly reasonable price, many of these feed manufacturers built their own processing plants. The same situation was prevalent in the edible-oil market, and many edible-oil users constructed soybean-processing firms. In consequence, all the main soybean-processing companies, with the exception of the A. E. Staley Company,[6] are vertically integrated and produce their own mixed feeds or edible-oil products or both. A list of some of these firms is as follows:

Allied Mills, Incorporated
Archer-Daniels-Midland Company
The Borden Company
Cargill, Incorporated
Central Soya, Incorporated
General Mills, Incorporated
The Glidden Company
Iowa Milling Company
Pillsbury Mills, Incorporated
Proctor and Gamble Company
Ralston and Purina Company
Spencer Kellogg
Swift and Company

The significance of vertical integration at the present time is important. Soybeans are relatively high priced in comparison to meal and oil (March 1952);[7] hence, it is difficult for a processor to make a profit. In consequence, many processors have either shut down their plants or

soybeans are being produced in southern states, such as Arkansas and Mississippi, and local meal demand is increasing. The development of the soybean industry in the South is thus being encouraged.

[5] These changes will be developed further at the end of this chapter.

[6] A. E. Staley operates an edible-oil refinery and produces mixed feeds. But these are minor operations when compared to the Company's over-all production of meal and oil.

[7] This is a temporary condition caused by the holding tendencies of the farmer, which raise the price of soybeans; the weak oil market, due to an excess supply of edible oils; and the ceiling price of meal, which has a tendency to keep meal prices below those that reflect the market demand for meal. In the long run, oil and meal prices determine the price of soybeans.

TABLE 25. Soybean-Processing Plants in the United States, 1950 *

State	Soybeans	Soybeans and Flaxseed	Soybeans and Peanuts	Soybeans and Copra	Soybeans and Corn	Soybeans and Cottonseed
Alabama						1
Arkansas	2					14
California	1	1		1	1	
Delaware	2					
Georgia						3
Illinois	29	2			1	1
Indiana	11	1			1	
Iowa	39	1				
Kansas	3	4				
Kentucky	4					
Louisiana						9
Michigan	2					
Minnesota	6	6				
Mississippi	2					17
Missouri	8					3
Nebraska	3					
New York	1	2				
North Carolina			1			5
North Dakota	1					
Ohio	15	1				
Oklahoma			1			7
Pennsylvania	2	1				
South Carolina						4
South Dakota		1				
Tennessee	3					6
Texas	1	1	1			13
Virginia	2				1	
Wisconsin	2					
Total	139	21	3	1	4	83

* Source: *Oil Mills Crushing Major Vegetable Oilseeds, 1950* (P.M.A., Fats and Oils Branch, U.S. Department of Agriculture).

adulterated their meal to avoid ceiling prices.[8] On the other hand, those feed manufacturers who have their own soybean-processing plants can be assured of their meal at ceiling prices. In spite of the unprofitable crushing margin, many of the large firms are expanding their processing plants or building new ones. Some processors are building new plants to the point where they are assured of a constant meal supply for their own mixed-feed products; but most processors are building larger plants or attempting to increase the capacity of their present processing

[8] A thorough examination of the effect of prices on processing will be undertaken in Chapter V.

plants primarily to take advantage of low per-unit operating costs. In consequence, the industry has even more crushing capacity than crushing supplies, and margins become even lower.

The question was put to those firms that had both a mixed-feed company and soybean-processing plants as to the possibilities of manufacturing their own edible-oil products – i.e. margarine and shortening. The most frequent answer given was that the marketing channels and type of direct consumer advertising needed for edible-oil products were a great deal different from the marketing channels of meal and the use of meal by the mixed-feed industry. In addition, the brands of margarine and shortening already in the market were fairly well established and competition would be difficult.

Another noticeable tendency of the processing industry is its flexibility. Twenty-one processing plants are so constructed as to allow for either flaxseed- or soybean-crushing; 83 processing plants crush soybeans and cottonseed; and others crush soybeans, peanuts, copra, corn, or a combination thereof (Table 25). The advantage of flexibility is

TABLE 26. The Estimated Soybean-Processing Capacities of the Nine Largest Operators, May 1945 and January 1951 *

Processor	1945		1951	
	Soybean Capacity per Day, in Thousand Bushels	Percentage of U.S. Total	Soybean Capacity per Day, in Thousand Bushels †	Percentage of U.S. Total ‡
A	59.5	10.9	92.4	12.2
B	58.5	10.7	57.8	7.1
C	50.6	9.2	49.5	6.6
D	49.0	8.9	49.5	6.6
E	28.4	5.2	46.2	6.1
F	19.1	3.5	36.3	4.4
G	17.0	3.1	33.0	4.4
H	16.3	3.0	33.0	4.4
I	12.7	2.3	26.4	3.5
Total	311.1	56.8	424.1	55.3

* The data for 1945 were obtained from J. W. Shollenberger and W. H. Goss, *Soybeans: Certain Agronomic, Physical, Chemical, Economic, and Industrial Aspects* (U.S. Bureau of Agricultural and Industrial Chemistry, Northern Regional Research Laboratory, Peoria, Illinois, 1947), p. 55. The data for 1951 were obtained through the help of George L. Levin, professional engineer.

† Figures based on "rated" capacities. Actual production may be 25 per cent to 50 per cent higher.

‡ Percentage of the total present "rated" production of all soybean processing plants.

obvious, for it enables processing plants to run at full capacity despite a shortage of any one particular oil crop. It further lessens seasonal swings. However, there are added technical and cost problems.[9]

Concentration of ownership is another factor that is evident in the historical development of the soybean-processing industry. In 1945 and 1951 over half of the total United States soybean-processing capacity was controlled by nine firms (Table 26). The significance of this fact is the tendency it shows toward industry integration; it also indicates the high cost of the original processing-plant investment.[10] It further suggests that the competitive position of different processing-plant locations may be equalized through the inner workings of companies owning soybean-processing plants in various parts of the country.

The entrance of the cooperatives into the soybean-processing industry is another discernible tendency. Over 14 per cent of the total soybean-processing plants in the United States are cooperatively owned and operated. They are located in the following states:

Iowa	7
Indiana	3
Kansas	2
Minnesota	2
Ohio	2
Illinois	1
Kentucky	1
Missouri	1
Wisconsin	1
Total	20

Thus far, the cooperative processing plants constructed have been small and locally owned. The significance of this fact is that, despite the trend to large-volume processing plants, there does seem to be a competitive place for small-volume processing plants to meet local needs.[11]

Finally, a tendency toward large-scale processing-plant construction and a growth in improved methods of solvent extraction are evident in the expansion of the United States soybean-processing industry. In 1944, 17 soybean-processing plants, each with a daily capacity of 200 tons or over, accounted for 48.2 per cent of the total crushing capacity

[9] These will be discussed in later sections of this chapter.
[10] This will be discussed in the cost section of the chapter.
[11] This will be discussed more fully in Chapter V.

Table 27. The Number of Soybean Plants in the United States on July 1, 1944, by Size *

Capacity, Tons per Day	Number of Plants	Percentage of Total Number	Total Estimated Capacity, in Thousand Bushels	Percentage of Total Capacity
Small plants †				
Less than 25	12	8.0	1,640	1.0
Medium-sized plants				
25–50	24	17.5	7,118	4.1
50–75	37	27.0	21,646	12.6
75–100	16	11.0	13,868	8.1
Large plants				
100–150	20	14.6	25,371	14.7
150–200	11	8.0	19,448	11.3
200–250	3	2.2	6,940	4.0
250–300	2	2.2	5,504	3.2
300–350	5	3.7	16,343	9.5
Over 350	7	5.1	54,355	31.5
Total	137	100.0	172,233	100.0

* Source: E. G. Schiffen, "Soybean Mills," *Soybean Digest,* Vol. 4, No. 12 (October 1944).

† The designation of plant size in this column is according to 1944 standards.

Table 28. The Number of Soybean Plants in the United States on January 1, 1951, by Size *

Capacity, Tons per Day †	Number of Plants	Percentage of Total Number	Total Estimated Capacity, in Thousand Bushels	Percentage of Total Capacity
One-expeller plants ‡				
Less than 25	14	10.5	3,500	1.5
Small plants				
25–75	60	45.1	45,000	19.6
Medium-sized plants				
75–200	17	12.8	34,000	14.6
200–300	33	24.8	99,000	42.9
Large plants				
300–500	5	3.8	25,000	10.9
Over 500	4	3.0	24,000	10.5
Total	133	100.0	230,500	100.0

* Analysis made with the help of George L. Levin, professional engineer.

† Figures are based on "rated" capacity, which is from 25 to 50 per cent below actual possible production.

‡ The designation of plant size in this column is according to 1950 standards.

(Table 27); whereas in 1951, 42 such processing plants accounted for 64.3 per cent of the total (Table 28). Also, the total crushing capacity increased by 170 million bushels from 1944 to 1951; however, the number of processing plants decreased by 4 (Tables 27 and 28). In addition, the intense competition among processors and the high price of oil during this period encouraged the use of the solvent extraction-method which, by its very nature, instigated the construction of more economical, large-scale-capacity processing plants.[12]

THE MINNESOTA PROCESSING INDUSTRY

Just as it took men of vision to establish the soybean-processing industry at Decatur, Illinois, the Minnesota industry also needed such leaders for its growth. Leaders were necessary to develop the crop, to build processing plants, and to find markets for the meal and oil produced. Mr. Joseph Sinaiko established the first processing plant west of the Mississippi. In the state of Minnesota, Mr. R. E. Hodgson, superintendent of the southeast experiment station at Waseca, Minnesota, began to work with the soybean crop some thirty-two years ago. Mr. John Evans of Montevideo was a pioneer producer, growing soybeans in Minnesota as early as 1917. Dr. James Hayward, head of the Archer-Daniels-Midland research staff, and Mr. Whitney Eastman, head of the Chemical Division of General Mills, pioneered in the utilization of soybean meal and oil, and helped convince the farmer that soybeans were a profitable crop. Businessmen such as Mr. Riley Lewis, the first full-time processor in the state; Mr. F. E. Benson, chief of the Soybean Division of Archer-Daniels-Midland; and Mr. Joseph Oberhauser, agricultural agent of the Milwaukee Railroad, all helped in establishing the processing industry in Minnesota.

Before 1939 the Archer-Daniels-Midland Company crushed soybeans in its linseed oil plant in Minneapolis. But this was a sporadic rather than a full-time operation.

The first soybean-processing plant was not constructed in the state of Minnesota until 1939. It was brought about by the inspiration of Mr. Riley Lewis and the encouragement of Mr. Harry Schultz, now vice-president of Pillsbury. Mr. Lewis discussed his processing-plant conception with several Mankato businessmen, who bought stock in the company in 1938.

[12] The discussion of the technical and cost problems occurs later in this chapter.

This processing plant, built in Mankato in 1939, was an expeller-type, with a crushing capacity of 40 tons per day. The plant manager was Mr. Frank Bergman, who was formerly with the Northwest Linseed Oil Company. Most of the time he did not have enough soybeans to run at processing capacity the year around. Hence flax was usually crushed from August to October and soybeans from October to January. Mr. Bergman bought most of the firm's soybeans from northern Iowa because they could be purchased in large carload lots from elevator operators, a practice avoiding the canvassing of wide areas in Minnesota. However, he encouraged the Minnesota farmer to grow more soybean varieties containing a greater percentage of oil.

The construction of the first soybean-processing plant was an additional impetus to Mr. Benson, Mr. Lewis, Dr. Hayward, Mr. Hodgson, Mr. Bergman, and Mr. Evans, who cooperated in spreading information to Minnesota farmers that would encourage them to grow enough soybeans to support a soybean-processing industry in the state. In the fall of 1939 a hundred meetings were held in cooperation with the Farm Bureau Federation in order to educate farmers to better methods of growing soybeans and to encourage them to increase their crop.

The original processing plant at Mankato was purchased by the Cooperative Poultry Association of the state of Washington in 1943 in order to ensure themselves an adequate supply of soybean meal during the acute wartime shortage.

As the soybean crop increased and better varieties were selected, other processors became interested in the industry. In 1944 the Consumers soybean expeller processing plant was built at Lakeville. In that same year, the Hubbard Milling Company constructed a processing plant at Preston, Minnesota. By 1945 these processing plants, together with the one at Mankato, were crushing over 2 million bushels of soybeans a year (Table 29). In 1947 the Poultry Cooperative Association sold its expeller processing plant to Honeymead Incorporated, which increased the expeller capacity to 100 tons a day. Also, in 1947, Cargill Incorporated established a combination solvent and expeller plant at Port Cargill, Minnesota. In the spring of 1949 Honeymead added a 250-tons-per-day, hexane-solvent operation to its expeller-plant capacity. The greatest expansion of the processing industry took place in Minnesota in 1950: a 25-tons-per-day trichlorethylene plant was constructed at Glencoe; another 25-ton trichlorethylene plant was built at

TABLE 29. Soybean Mills in Operation in Minnesota, October 1, 1945 *

Firm	Date Founded	Total Crushing Capacity, Bushels
Archer-Daniels-Midland Co. (Minneapolis) †		
Mankato Soybean Products (Mankato)	1939‡	
Consumer's Soybean Mills (Lakeville)	1944	
Hubbard Milling Co. (Preston)	1944	
		2,383,000

* Source: *Soybean Digest*, 1945.
† Primarily a linseed oil operation.
‡ Bought by Cooperative Poultry Association in 1943.

TABLE 30. Soybean Production in Minnesota, Actual and Potential, December 1951

Firm	Potential Soybeans Crushed, Tons per Day	Percentage of Total Capacity	Production, Bushels per Year: Actual	Production, Bushels per Year: Potential
Honeymead Products, Inc. (Mankato)	350	34.3		
Archer-Daniels-Midland Co. (Mankato)	300	29.4		
Cargill, Inc. (Port Cargill)	190	18.6		
Consumer's Soybean Mills, Inc. (Lakeville)	80	7.8		
Preston Soya Mills, Inc. (Preston)	50	4.9		
Farmers Co-op Elevator Assoc. (Blooming Prairie)	25	2.5		
Farmers & Merchants Milling Co., Inc. (Glencoe)	25	2.5		
Tri-County Cooperative Soybean Assoc. (Dawson) ..	...*	...		
Total	1,020	100.0	9,800,000	12,240,000

* 50 tons; not operated in 1951.

Blooming Prairie; and a 300-ton hexane plant was erected by the Archer-Daniels-Midland Company at Mankato. The newest processing plant is a 50-ton trichlorethylene firm which was completed at Dawson in November 1951, and which brings the state total to eight soybean processing plants (Fig. 26). The state's processing capacity is now approximately 12 million bushels a year (Table 30).

In the description of the growth of the soybean-processing industry in Minnesota, the primary emphasis thus far has been placed on personalities rather than on processing plants and processing capacity. This was done purposely to demonstrate that despite certain economic factors favorable to the development of the soybean crop and processing industry in Minnesota, the inertia of producers, processors, and utilizers has to be overcome by men of vision and leadership. One might call them Schumpeter's "entrepreneurs."

FIGURE 26. Location of Minnesota Soybean-Processing Plants, 1951.

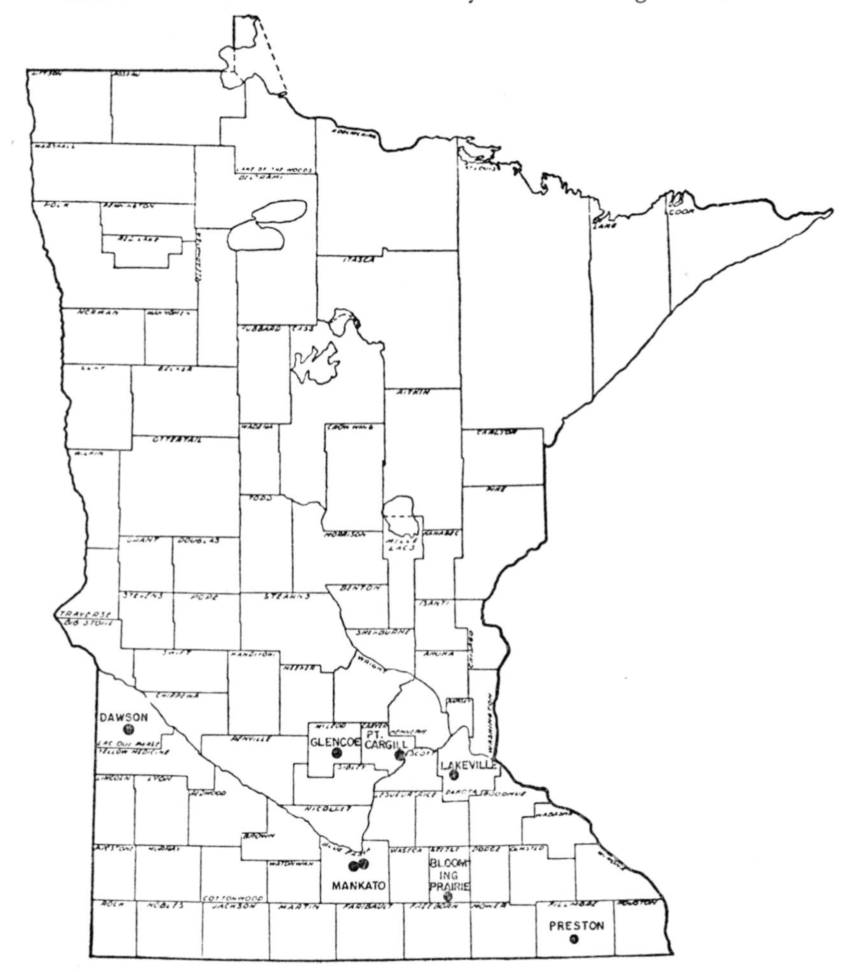

It is evident that the economic tendencies illustrated by the development of the soybean-processing industry in Minnesota parallel those of the national processing industry. Vertical integration is present in Minnesota, as three firms in the state have their own brands of mixed feeds, which utilize much of the soybean meal they produce. Three of the state's firms crush flax as well as soybeans, a fact emphasizing the flexibility of the industry. This flexibility is of special importance to Minnesota producers and processors as both flax and soybeans are prominent oilseed crops in the state.

Two of Minnesota's main processing plants are owned by companies having such concerns in several states, and two of Minnesota's eight plants are cooperatively owned and operated. The national economic tendencies of concentration of ownership and the cooperative movement within the soybean industry are illustrated by these four processing plants.

The significance of these economic tendencies in the processing industry on the state level is the same as on the national. Stated briefly, these tendencies indicate the need of large-scale, efficient processing plants, with a maximum guaranteed outlet for the processed products – especially meal. To build such processing plants, a large amount of capital is necessary, which usually means a limit to the number of firms able to enter into the industry, or, in other words, means concentration of ownership.[13] The flexibility that is helpful in avoiding shutdowns requires not only the ability to crush more than one oilseed crop but the ability to have processing plants in several locations to take advantage of specific area gains and minimize specific area losses.[14] This too leads to the dominance of large, well-integrated, national agricultural businesses in the soybean-processing industry. At the same time the growth of small, cooperatively and privately owned soybean-processing plants indicates a need of such firms on a local, limited-size basis.

Before examining the competitive position of these various-sized processing plants in Minnesota, the technical development and financial structure of these firms must be analyzed.[15]

[13] Financial and cost problems of the industry will be discussed in a later section of this chapter.

[14] Location advantages and disadvantages will be discussed in Chapter V.

[15] The competitive position of the Minnesota processor will be discussed in Chapter V.

TECHNICAL DEVELOPMENT

Technically, the main innovation of recent importance in the soybean-processing industry is the solvent extraction-method. This procedure is rapidly replacing the expeller and hydraulic processes (Fig. 27 and Table 31). The chief economic advantage of the solvent method is the additional pound and a half of oil the solvent extracts from a bushel of soybeans. The saving is illustrated by the following computation:

In 1951, assume the price of meal is $65 a ton, or 3.25 cents a pound; the price of oil, 20 cents a pound; and a bushel of soybeans (60 pounds), $2.80.

Expeller Method		*Solvent Method*	
Oil yield/bu. = 8.5 lbs. or	$1.70	Oil yield/bu. = 10.0 lbs. or	$2.00
Meal yield/bu. = 50.0 lbs. or	1.63	Meal yield/bu. = 48.5 lbs. or	1.58
Total	$3.33	Total	$3.58
Minus cost of soybeans	2.80	Minus cost of soybeans	2.80
Crushing margin	$0.53	Crushing margin	$0.78
Minus cost of processing	x	Minus cost of processing	y
Net profit	$0.53 − x	Net profit	$0.78 − y

In 1951 the solvent method would save the processor 25 cents a bushel, plus or minus the difference in processing costs between the two processes.[16] Of course, in 1952 the price of oil has dropped to 10 cents a pound and the price of meal has risen to $74 a ton, or 3.7 cents a pound, the advantage of the solvent process thus being narrowed. Nevertheless, the incentive to change from the expeller operation to a solvent one is still important. All the processing-plant construction in Minnesota since 1947 has been of the solvent-extraction type.

In order to analyze the cost structure of the processing industry in Minnesota, the technical problems of the different processes that help determine cost variations among processing plants must be examined.

Hydraulic pressing is the oldest method of obtaining oil and meal from soybeans, but it is little used today (Fig. 28). It works on the principle of the hydraulic ram and operates like an ordinary machine-shop press (Fig. 28). Because the hydraulic process is not in operation in Minnesota, no technical analysis of this method is needed for this study.

The expeller or screw-press method was up to 1950 the most im-

[16] Costs will be discussed in the final section of this report.

FIGURE 27. Proportion of Soybeans Processed by Specified Methods, United States, 1937–1950.

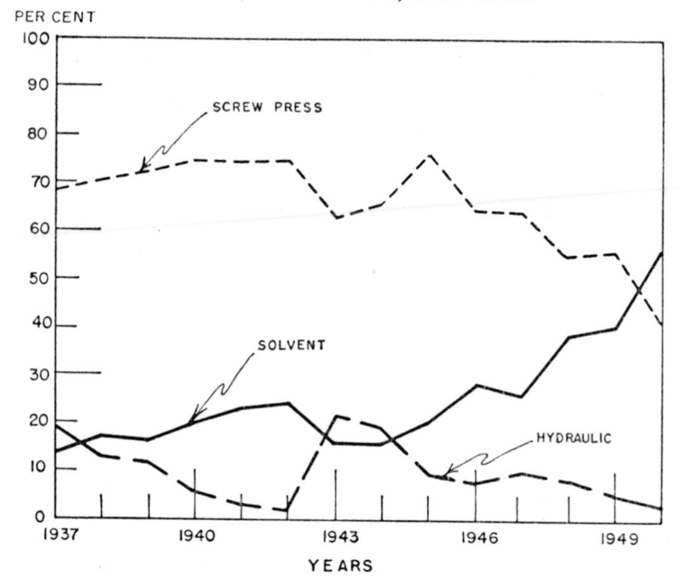

TABLE 31. A Summary of Soybean-Processing Facilities and Operation Status, Excluding Mills Crushing Soybeans Temporarily or Less Than Half Their Operating Time, United States, May 1945 and January 1951 *

Type of Mill	1945 Number of Plants	1945 Capacity, in Thousand Bushels	1945 Percentage of U.S. Total †	1951 Number of Plants	1951 Capacity, in Thousand Bushels	1951 Percentage of U.S. Total ‡
Screw presses						
Anderson expellers ..	356	228.7	41.8	356	240	29.8
French screw presses	174	124.0	22.7	174	132	16.3
Unclassified	16	12.8	2.3	16	12	1.5
Total	546	365.5	66.8	546	384	47.6
Solvent extraction						
French	...	....	...	31	211	26.5
Anderson	...	....	...	14	43	5.3
Blaw-Knox	...	....	...	11	89	11.0
Allis Chalmers	...	....	...	7	43	5.3
Crown Iron Works ..	...	....	...	5	5	.6
Combination plants ..	...	....	...	4	7	.9
Miscellaneous	...	....	...	2	18	2.2
Total	36	172.0	31.4	74	416	51.8

* Analysis made with the help of George L. Levin, professional engineer.
† 1.8 per cent capacity used the hydraulic process.
‡ 0.6 per cent capacity used the hydraulic process.

FIGURE 28. Soybean Oil Meal Processing, Hydraulic Method.

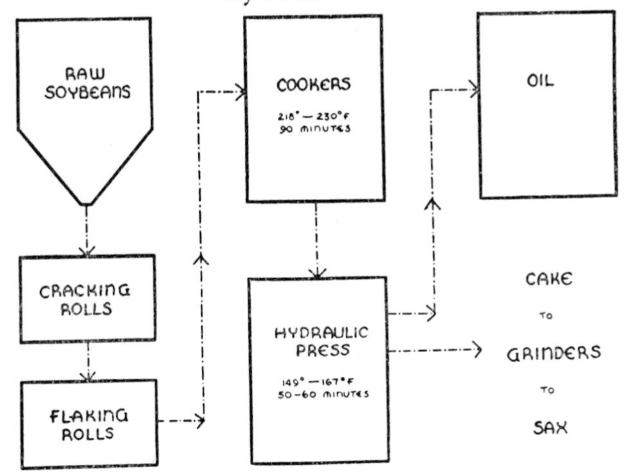

Source: Archer-Daniels-Midland Company.

FIGURE 29. Soybean Oil Meal Processing, Expeller Method.

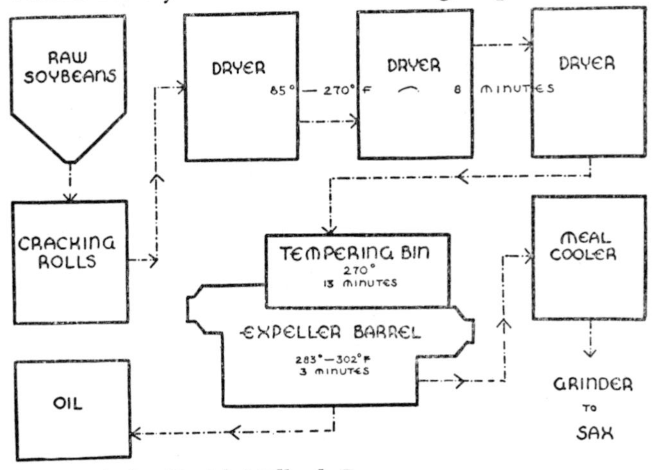

Source: Archer-Daniels-Midland Company.

portant means of obtaining oil and meal from soybeans. The production flow in this process is illustrated in Figure 29.

The problems inherent in the screw-press method of extraction are principally three in number: obtaining a uniform quality of meal and oil, high degrees of oil content, and moisture control. The proper tightening of the jaw on the expeller barrel should allow a maximum amount of oil to be pressed from the soybean (Fig. 29). However, if the jaw is too tight in the attempt to increase oil yield, the pressure may result in burnt meal. On the other hand, if the jaw is too loose, the cost of the loss of oil may be greater than the advantage of the increased meal output. Finally, in returning moisture to the meal, a constant check must be made. If too little moisture is added to the meal, to replace the moisture content lost during the crushing and toasting process, the processor's net returns will be reduced. If too much moisture is added, grinding of the meal may be difficult, and the processor will have violated the trading rules.

The hexane-solvent, continuous-extraction process is now the most important method of obtaining oil and meal from the soybean. The production flow of this process is illustrated in Figure 30.

FIGURE 30. Soybean Oil Meal Processing, Extraction Method.

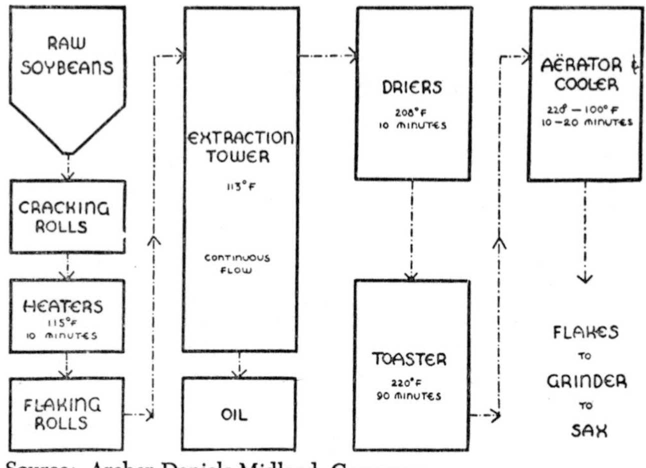

Source: Archer-Daniels-Midland Company.

The problems inherent in the continuous, solvent extraction-method include not only those of the expeller process—oil yields, uniform quality of meal and oil, and moisture control—but others as well—solvent loss and solvent explosion. The moisture of the beans affects the whole process. If the soybeans are too wet, they gum up the cracking rolls and do not allow proper flaking (Fig. 30). In addition, if the flakes are not of the proper thickness, they in turn do not permit maximum extraction of the oil. If the soybeans are too dry, they are pulverized by the cracking rolls, allow improper flaking, and permit too many fine particles in the meal. Moisture also affects the final meal product. If the meal is too moist, improper grinding takes place, and trading rules are violated. If the moisture content is too low, the processor is not maximizing profits. Solvent loss is another problem in this process. If any "plug ups" occur in the process, much of the solvent can be wasted. In addition, any loss of solvent on the premises increases the danger of explosion. Control panels, underground storage tanks, and fire walls are all methods used to minimize the danger of hexane explosion.

The trichlorethylene-solvent extraction-process is similar to that of the hexane process with the exception that trichlorethylene is less explosive and is a heavier solvent. However, recent studies at the University of Minnesota indicate that soybean meal produced by the trichlorethylene process is toxic to cattle. The problem of toxicity has been the chief deterrent to the development of this solvent extraction-method.

Other new developments in the technique of soybean-processing revolve around different methods of solvent extraction and various applications of steam or pressure cooking. One recent development is the DeSmet process, which can be used not only for the solvent extraction of soybeans but for other oil seed crops as well. Before this process, most oil seeds, because of their higher oil contents, had to be prepressed by expellers before solvent extraction was feasible. This meant additional pressing, cracking, and toasting equipment, which raised the investment cost of a flexible processing plant. Two processing plants have ordered the DeSmet equipment from Europe, although neither is in operation at this writing (March 1952). This and other methods in the industry are being developed to make the oilseed industry more efficient and more flexible.

The technical problems of the soybean-processing industry having been examined, we may now turn to the cost of processing.

PROCESSING COSTS

Large-scale, solvent extraction processing plants were developed not only because of the greater oil yields possible, but also because of the low cost of operation. However, the original investment cost for such a process is extremely high. For a processing plant with a capacity of

300 tons per day, the cost, including equipment, installation, buildings and service, but excluding storage facilities for soybeans, is approximately $1,000,000 (Appendix, Table 21).

Although no thorough operating cost study has been made of the soybean-processing industry on a national level, certain general cost trends are recognized. Because of the high original-investment cost of a solvent processing-plant, its over-all processing costs are thought to be slightly higher per bushel than those of an expeller processing-plant of comparable size. This was taken into account when the government set the allowable crushing margins for various types of processing plants during World War II. They were as indicated in Table 32.

TABLE 32. Soybean Processing Margin by Size and Type of Plant, 1943–1944

Type and Size	Cents per Bushel
Hydraulic press	
Large	29
Medium	30
Small	31
Expeller or screw press	
Large	24
Medium	26
Small	28
Solvent extraction	
Large	29
Medium	30
Small	31

It is to be noted that costs usually decrease as the size of the plant increases. Thus far no optimum size-limit for equipment has been found. Some single processing units are rated as high as 600 tons per day, which means that the actual operational capacity is even higher. Many processors feel that the added capacity of a processing plant over 300 tons per day reduces processing costs per bushel only slightly.

The range of processing costs for different firms is very wide. The costs of twenty cooperative plants in the United States range from a low per-bushel processing cost of 16.7 cents to a high of 48.4 cents, and a weighted average of 25.5 cents.

MINNESOTA PROCESSING COSTS

The general cost tendencies noted above were substantiated by a cost study of six of Minnesota's seven soybean-processing plants operat-

TABLE 33. The Processing Costs of Six Minnesota Soybean Plants, Percentage Breakdown and Actual Cents-per-Bushel Range, 1951

	Percentage of Total Costs, by Company						Cost, Cents per Bushel	
	A	B	C	D	E	F	Lowest	Highest
Current operating cost								
Plant payroll	28.8	23.6	22.4	27.2	24.4	40.0*	7.13	15.60
Fuel	9.2	12.8	5.8	7.7	2.4	7.0	0.75	6.02
Power	4.1	6.4	6.3	4.7	9.7	10.0	1.24	3.01
Solvent	6.1	9.4	7.9	6.0	....	....	1.58	4.42
Repairs and supplies	9.4	0.6	13.8	13.6	10.6	15.0	0.27	5.10
Mill expense and miscellaneous	1.9	0.4	....	3.3	3.9	....	0.21	1.18
Total	59.5	53.2	56.2	62.5	51.0	72.0	11.18	35.33
Fixed and general								
Office payroll and sales	19.4	7.4	7.8	18.8	15.5	....	1.86	10.50
Depreciation	7.8	14.5	12.3	13.6	9.6	16.0	2.91	6.83
Taxes	1.8	1.5	2.6	1.8	2.6	5.0	0.48	1.00
Truck depreciation and expense	8.3	....	0.2	....	6.3	....	0.05	4.50
Insurance	1.3	1.2	2.8	3.0	4.2	3.0	0.57	1.29
Interest	0.2	16.9	5.3	....	4.2	3.5	0.10	7.91
Advertising	1.1	0.5	0.6	....	3.4	....	0.14	1.02
Assessment and dues	....	0.1	0.1	....	0.4	0.5	0.06	0.13
Rent	....	....	1.1	....	2.0	....	0.27	0.60
Other	0.6	4.7	11.0	0.3	0.8	....	0.08	2.63
Total	40.5	46.8	43.8	37.5	49.0	28.0	6.52	36.28
Total processing cost †	100.0	100.0	100.0	100.0	100.0	100.0	17.70	71.61

* Includes both office and plant payroll.

† The actual range in total operating costs between the firms lowest and highest on this scale is from 20.0 to 54.1 cents per bushel. The weighted average is 26.5 cents per bushel.

ing in 1951 (Table 33). Several limitations in using the Minnesota data may be noted. Actual cents-per-bushel costs were obtained from these companies on the understanding that no individual costs would be linked to any particular firm. The total costs of each firm, therefore, were broken down on a percentage basis rather than on a monetary basis. Actual monetary costs were used to illustrate the cost range for a particular item. The lowest cost for each item is that cost which is the lowest among the six firms. Similarly, the highest cost for each item is that cost which is the highest among the six firms. In consequence, the total of the lowest costs of all items is a lower processing cost than the over-all low cost of a particular firm. The same is true of the highest processing cost.

Other limitations of the data include various accounting problems. Each firm has its own type of accounting procedure; for this study, consequently, several costs were arbitrarily assigned to general categories (Table 33). Several of the processing plants are combination types in that they have both expeller and solvent operations. These firms have found it difficult to separate out costs for each process; so in many items these costs are combined. In addition, some firms have grain elevators and mixed-feed plants combined with their soybean-processing operations. Hence, allocating labor, fuel, and power costs over these three businesses is a highly inexact process.

Keeping these limitations in mind, it is still possible to draw several inferences from these data. In the first place, the wide range of the actual processing costs in the state, from 20 cents a bushel to 54.1 cents a bushel, and the theoretical spread, from 17.7 cents a bushel to 71.6 cents a bushel, compare with the wide range noted in the cooperative study. The actual weighted averages of the two groups of firms are also fairly close. The cooperative processing weighted-average cost for the nation was 25.5 cents, whereas for Minnesota it was 26.5 cents a bushel. In essence, from the limited cost data available, the costs of Minnesota's processing industry are about the same as those of other areas.

Cost differences among the Minnesota firms suggest some of the possible trends in future processing-plant construction, and the strength and weakness of the firms already established in the state.

Plant payroll is the most important cost item for all firms. The cost saving of the solvent extraction-method is attributed to the need of fewer men to supervise and run large processing units. Surprisingly, even though there is a wide range in actual labor costs (from 7 to 15.5 cents), the percentage importance of plant payroll costs is very similar in all firms (Table 33).[17]

Office payroll and sales costs vary the most among the firms, both in monetary and percentage terms. This variation is due to the problem of allocating administrative costs to firms which have a central home office. Furthermore, the small processing plants have no sales people at all. Selling is primarily order-taking for such firms.

The cost of solvent among solvent processing plants A through D does not vary much percentagewise, but in monetary terms, there is a 3-cents-per-bushel saving between the firms lowest and highest in cost. This additional cost for plants using solvent is partially offset by the additional cost of the power required by the expeller process. Maintenance is also more costly for expeller than for solvent operations because expellers tend to get clogged and need repair or replacement.

The insurance cost should be relatively higher for hexane-solvent plants because of the possibility of explosion, but such is not the case. In fact, the rates on some expeller and trichlorethylene plants are higher than on the hexane-solvent plants.

Depreciation costs also vary considerably among the various-sized processing plants because of the differences in the original investment costs.

The expenditure on interest varies a great deal because of the changing amount of each firm's soybean, meal, and oil inventories, and also of their borrowings for the construction of processing plants. On the whole, interest costs in all but one of the firms were extremely low – a fact indicating not only the high liquidity of the inventories carried but also a conservative hedging policy.

Repairs and supplies are fairly uniform costs for all firms percentagewise with the exception of one. This firm evidently was allocating some of this expense in the form of depreciation.

The general cost tendencies indicate that the large-volume, hexane processing plants are more efficient, and, despite high original-investment costs, have the lowest per-bushel operating costs in the state. The small-volume, trichlorethylene plants prove to be the most costly because they have the disadvantage of having a high original-investment cost (approximately $250,000) without the labor-saving advantage of

[17] Plant F's figures are not broken down between office and plant payroll costs.

the large-volume, solvent extraction plants. These over-all cost tendencies within the state must be kept in mind in the next chapter when the competitive position of the Minnesota processing industry is examined.

The diversity of specific costs indicates a wide variation in management's emphasis in the day-to-day processing plant operations. On the whole, in the operation of a large-volume, solvent extraction plant, savings can be made in office and plant payroll and in maintenance costs which more than offset additional depreciation and solvent costs. From a purely cost standpoint, therefore, the hexane-solvent extraction-method is in the strongest competitive position within the state and will be the type of operation used if further processing expansion takes place. This additional construction may tend to be in the form of enlarging present processing facilities rather than building new ones, because it is usually less costly to add additional equipment to present plant facilities.

SUMMARY

In summary, the capacity of the soybean industry in the United States has increased fivefold in the last decade, and much of it is unused throughout the year either because of the lack of soybean supplies or unfavorable crushing margins. This situation has led to the construction of more-efficient processing plants. Such processing plants are usually large-volume, hexane-solvent plants, requiring enormous capital outlays for construction. This high original-investment cost together with the advantages of vertical integration has led to the entrance of large-scale agricultural firms into the industry to the point where concentration of ownership is discernible. As the industry matures and competition becomes keener, these trends will be even more pronounced.

Competition and the construction of processing plants of similar type should also decrease the processing costs for soybean firms and narrow the wide differences in the total processing costs and in individual cost items evidenced in the Minnesota study.

However, the fact that wide variations in processing costs can exist in the industry and that small cooperatively and privately owned processing plants are being constructed indicates that the factors of transportation, storage, central market, and price formulation greatly affect the competitive position of processing firms in this industry. These factors will be analyzed in the next chapter, in order that we may arrive at the competitive position of the Minnesota soybean processor.

CHAPTER V

Factors Affecting the Competitive Position of the Minnesota Soybean Processor

THE first part of this chapter will be concerned with transportation and storage as they affect the competitive position of the processor. An analysis will follow the influence of trading on the central market and the effect of such trading on the Minnesota soybean industry. The next section will deal with the effect of price formulation upon the processing industry. Finally, all these factors will be brought together in an analysis of crushing margins.[1]

The principle of comparative advantage has thus far in this study been the basis for the description and analysis of soybean production, utilization, and processing. "Each area tends to produce those products for which its ratio of advantage is greatest as compared with other areas, or its ratio of advantage is least, up to the point where the land may be needed by some products less advantaged in the area in order to meet the demand for them at such prices as will come to prevail under such circumstances."[2] The approach has been empirical, with emphasis placed upon historical trends and upon the factors bringing about changes in supply, demand, and processing.

The broad economic concepts of Von Thunen and the location theory of Weber, together with the equilibrium theory, are useful tools in the examination of the mutual interdependence of the factors of transportation, storage, commodity markets, and price formulation, and the relation of these factors to the location of the Minnesota soybean industry. However, these tools are not serviceable if used only in the

[1] Crushing margins are determined by the relation between the purchase price of soybeans and the selling price of meal and oil.

[2] J. D. Black, *Production Economics* (New York: Henry Holt & Co., 1926), p. 137.

context of static equilibrium analysis. Therefore, in the examination of the dynamic processing industry of Minnesota, these economic theories will be used in a dynamic fashion in the sense that they will provide a mental framework for the realistic analysis of each of the changing variables that affect the Minnesota soybean processor.

TRANSPORTATION

The fact that the development of the soybean processing industry was centered at Decatur, Illinois, led to the establishment of a Decatur price basis. As the industry expanded, it was natural for competitors to use the Decatur price as a common denominator when quoting prices to prospective purchasers. The customer could readily understand his purchase advantage or disadvantage without going into the rate structure. The most advantageous location of a processor is at an extreme distance from Decatur, where local soybean supplies are available and where meal is sold locally at the Decatur price plus freight, allowing the processor to retain the added freight revenue as profit. The feed manufacturer usually is not concerned about the freight advantage or disadvantage of the processor. Instead, he is more interested in obtaining information on the price his feed competitor pays for soybean meal.

From the above, it is obvious that the price of shipping soybean meal from Decatur, Illinois, to points in the United States has an enormous influence in determining the profitability of various processing locations (Appendix, Table 22, and Fig. 31). Other factors affecting the transportation and location analysis have been listed as follows:

"1. The necessity of locating so as to be able to reach many widespread markets.
2. The existence of the processing-in-transit privilege.
3. The 5 per cent weight loss in processing.
4. The nonapplication of the through rate to soybean oil under transit.
5. The relationship between rates on soybeans and those on processed products." [3]

In regard to the first point, the largest-volume processing plants are located in Illinois. This is the case because the supply of soybeans available in Illinois together with available meal and oil markets developed the industry in Illinois and led to the establishment of Decatur, Illinois,

[3] E. C. Hedlund, "The Transportation Economics of the Soybean Processing Industry," unpublished Ph.D. thesis, University of Illinois, 1948.

FIGURE 31. Price of Shipping Soybean Meal per Ton from Decatur, Illinois, December 1951.

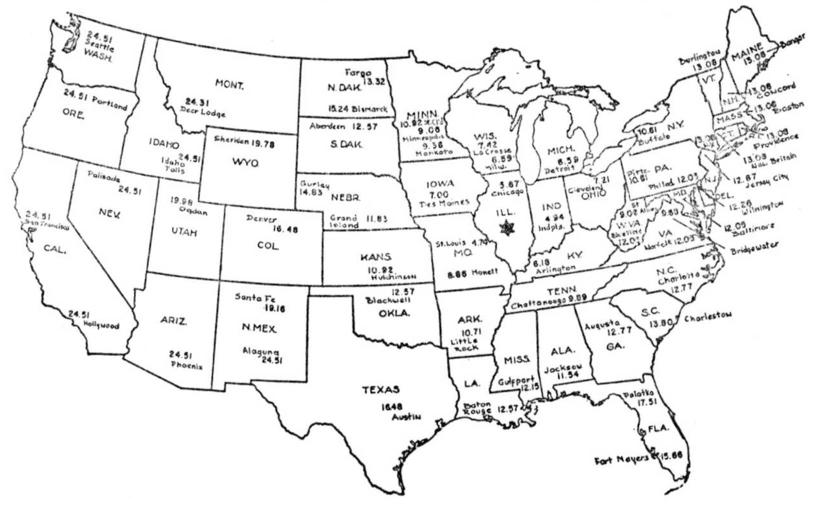

as the "pricing" point of the industry. Therefore, Illinois processors can consider the nation their meal market. Illinois, for example, has a relatively small number of soybean mills; yet the state's processing capacity is the largest in the United States (Table 34). Though Iowa has many more processing mills, its processing capacity is less than that of Illinois (Table 34). Iowa processing-plant production is limited to the local market and the markets to the west that are not competitive with the Decatur location. Minnesota's market is even further limited because of its northern and western location. However, as these local processors expand their operations within their respective states, they decrease the national market for the Illinois processors. In consequence, the processing capacity of Illinois is now overexpanded.

The processing-in-transit privilege is another important transportation factor. This privilege allows a through traffic rate for shipping soybeans from the point of origin to the final consumer of the meal regardless of the location of the processing plant. But this transit privilege applies only to the meal (some 80 per cent of the soybean by weight). Therefore, the closer the processing plant to the supply of soybeans, the less the inbound-freight cost to the processor on that portion of the soybean that is used for oil and that portion that constitutes the 5 per cent processing waste.

TABLE 34. The Capacity of Soybean Mills in Specified Areas, Excluding Mills Crushing Soybeans Temporarily or Less Than Half Their Operating Time, May 1945 and 1950 *

Area	1945			1950		
	Number of Mills	Soybean Capacity, Bushels per Day	Percentage of U.S. Total Capacity	Number of Mills	Soybean Capacity, Bushels per Day	Percentage of U.S. Total Capacity
Illinois	33	193,215	35.3	29	243,215	38.6
Iowa	36	107,880	19.7	39	110,681	17.6
Ohio	17	63,630	11.6	15	76,754	12.2
Indiana	16	56,723	10.4	11	54,010	8.6
Missouri	7	18.700	3.4	8	24,358	3.9
Kentucky, Tennessee, Arkansas	8	21,050	3.8	9	57,064	9.0
Kansas, Nebraska	14	25,630	4.7	9	15,950	2.6
Wisconsin, Minnesota, North Dakota, Michigan, South Dakota	17	29,490	5.4	7†	21,228†	3.4†
New York, Pennsylvania, Virginia, California, Colorado, Delaware	12	31,200	5.7	...	......	...
Total	160	547,518	100.0	127	603,260	95.9

* Source: *Facts for Industry, Fats and Oils,* Bureau of the Census.
† Minnesota alone for 1950 figures.

As railroad rates increase for soybean, oil, and meal shipments, the transportational advantages of local markets and local supplies become more important to the development of the processing industry (Appendix, Table 23). The consumption of soybean meal at continually higher levels in the processing and producing states, evidenced in Chapter III, has been due, in part, to the increased transportation costs and the greater emphasis the processors have placed on the local market as an outlet for their meal (Appendix, Tables 24 and 25).

The relation between traffic rates on soybeans and those on soybean processed goods will also determine the location of the processing industry toward either the raw material or the processed meal and oil markets. These rate relations have fluctuated somewhat the past few years (Appendix, Table 23). However, the large livestock population in the Corn Belt, together with the fact that soybean meal is the most important product of the soybean, leads to the conclusion that the soybean processing industry will continue to expand where the combination of soybean production and livestock population exists. It is true that soybean oil does not have a transit privilege, and that transportation costs to the processor are high when the oil is shipped at a flat rate against a Decatur pricing basis; but such disadvantages, at present, do not outweigh the other meal-transportation advantages indicated.

MINNESOTA TRANSPORTATION

The transportation factor is one of the most important elements in the determination of the competitive position of the Minnesota processing industry. The broad transportational tendencies mentioned in the preceding paragraphs are best applied to an analysis of the Minnesota location by specific examples.

Buffalo, New York. Assume that soybeans are produced at St. James, Minnesota; processed at Mankato, Minnesota; and the meal is sold at Buffalo, New York. The processor usually has a transit privilege for the meal he produces; or, in other words, for 80 per cent of the soybeans bought, a through traffic rate is permissible. The interstate traffic rate from St. James to Mankato is 13½ cents per hundredweight. Transit rates exist from St. James to the terminal point of Chicago; but from Chicago to Buffalo a proportional rate is used. The total traffic rate per 100 pounds from Mankato to Buffalo, using transit from St. James, is as follows:

St. James to Chicago	= 38¢ + 6 per cent + 3 per cent[4]
(Plus) Chicago to Buffalo	= 33½¢ + 6 per cent + 3 per cent
Transit (minus) St. James to Mankato	= 13½¢ + 6 per cent + 3 per cent
Mankato to Buffalo, using St. James transit, total	= 58¢ + 6 per cent + 3 per cent[5]
Flat rate from Mankato to Buffalo via Chicago	= 63¢ + 6 per cent + 3 per cent

The significance of this example is twofold. In the first place, it illustrates how costly it is to ship meal to the eastern part of the United States from Minnesota. The cost of shipping a ton of soybean meal from Decatur, Illinois, to Buffalo is $10.61 minus the inbound freight from the farmer to the processor at Decatur; whereas the shipping cost from Mankato is $12.66, or a Decatur advantage of $2.05 per ton, less inbound transit (Appendix, Table 22, and Fig. 31). Hence, the eastern market is not a favorable one for Minnesota processors. In the second place, the example illustrates that the inbound cost of buying soybeans would be the 20 per cent of the billing not applicable for transit; or, in other words, 20 per cent of 14.7 cents (the total rate from St. James to Mankato per hundred pounds of soybeans). Therefore, the closer the soybeans are to the processing plant, the less the 20 per cent inbound freight cost.

Fargo, North Dakota. Assume that beans again are produced at St. James, Minnesota; processed at Mankato, Minnesota; but sold at Fargo, North Dakota, in the form of meal.

The total traffic rate to Fargo per hundred pounds of meal, using the St. James transit rate, is as follows:

St. James to Fargo	= 37¢ + 6 per cent + 3 per cent
Transit (minus) St. James to Mankato	= 13½¢ + 6 per cent + 3 per cent
Mankato to Fargo, using St. James transit, total freight cost per 100 pounds	= 23½¢ + 6 per cent + 3 per cent[6]

[4] The 6 per cent refers to an emergency traffic charge which is in lieu of a 15 per cent cost-of-living increase asked by the railroads from the I.C.C. The 3 per cent refers to a transportation tax. (March 1952.)

[5] The transit rate to Buffalo is determined by CNW 17043-F, Item 250 WTL 330N and CFA 535B.

[6] Obtained from Item 4090 WTL. 25-F, WTL. 23-A.

Translated into tons (2,000 pounds), the total freight cost is $5.12 per ton of meal from Mankato to Fargo. The Decatur rate to Fargo is $13.32 a ton minus inbound freight, or a Mankato advantage of $8.20 a ton minus the Decatur processor's inbound transit (Appendix, Table 22, and Fig. 31).

The significance of this illustration is the unusual shipping advantage the Minnesota processor has over the Decatur processor in selling meal to nearby western states. This transportation advantage is also evident in a comparison of the Minnesota location with that of Iowa, but the Minnesota transportation advantage over Iowa is less than that over Decatur because Iowa processing plants are closer to the Minnesota and western state meal-markets.

St. Cloud, Minnesota. Assume once again that soybeans are produced at St. James, Minnesota; processed at Mankato; and the meal is sold at St. Cloud, Minnesota. In this case, the inbound freight rate is only 11 cents from St. James to Mankato because it is an intrastate rate.[7] The outgoing rate from Mankato to St. Cloud is also an intrastate rate, amounting to 22 cents per hundred pounds. Therefore, the total transportation cost per hundred pounds, using transit, from St. James to St. Cloud via Mankato is as follows:

St. James to St. Cloud = 22¢ + 3 per cent[8]
Transit (minus) St. James to Mankato = 11¢ + 3 per cent
Mankato to St. Cloud, using St. James transit, total = 11¢ + 3 per cent[9]

Translated from per-hundred-pound units to per tons, the total transportation charge is $2.26 from Mankato to St. Cloud. The Decatur shipping cost to St. Cloud is $10.92 a ton minus the cost of inbound transit,

[7] Intrastate rates refer to shipments originating and terminating within the state.

[8] The 6 per cent emergency charge has not been authorized for intrastate rates. This and other special privileges for intrastate rates may be attacked by the courts as infringements of interstate commerce.

[9] In addition, Minnesota has a further advantage of being allowed a continuous mile rating over the shortest possible route, using not more than three railroads at interchange points where facilities for interchange are available. This becomes the rate even if not used by the processor. An example of this would be the mileage from St. James to St. Cloud, Minnesota. The short line is the Omaha RR to Merriam, the Milwaukee and St. Louis to Minneapolis, and the Great Northern from there to St. Cloud. The natural route is 1/10 mile longer, being from St. James to Minneapolis on the Omaha, and the Great Northern to St. Cloud. Sometimes this slight difference will put a processor on a breaking point of a lower rate. A processor ships over the natural route, but his rate is determined by the shortest route of not more than three railroad combinations.

or a Mankato advantage of $8.62 a ton minus the cost of Decatur inbound transit.

The significance of this example is twofold. It strikingly illustrates the transportation advantage of a Minnesota soybean processor who can sell his meal production within the state. Secondly, it illustrates the favorable Minnesota intrastate rates.

Chicago soybean prices. Transportation affects the purchase of soybeans by the processor. Soybeans are usually purchased by the processor or his broker on a track basis. In other words, the purchase price is based upon the location of the soybeans, and the purchaser assumes the transportation charge. The basing point of his quotation is the cash price, track Chicago. If the transportation rate for soybeans from St. James to Chicago is 24.8 cents a bushel, the processor would offer to buy the soybeans on the basis of the Chicago cash price, less 25 cents a bushel freight cost, or the approximate track country-point price at St. James.

The above procedure is used rather than that of buying the soybeans on the basis of an inter- or intrastate rate from St. James to Mankato and then figuring the cost from Mankato to Chicago because it is a more convenient method and avoids later adjustments and misunderstandings between the buyer and seller. Furthermore, Chicago is used as a basing point for the purchase of soybeans because it is a grain terminal for soybeans and other commodities, and because the location there of a Chicago futures market permits hedging operations. The question arises whether it would be better to use positions such as Decatur as points of delivery for soybeans because this location and other crop centers are in the path of the normal physical movement of the crop.[10]

Qualifications. There are several other aspects of transportation that qualify and modify the picture presented by the previous examples. In addition to the intrastate, interstate, and in-transit rates used in determining freight costs for buying soybeans and selling meal and oil, there are specific geographical rates on commodities shipped from terminal locations. The terminal markets include Chicago, Minneapolis, Peoria, St. Louis, Sioux City, Omaha, Kansas City, Duluth, and Milwaukee. The actual freight cost for a bushel of soybeans from the terminal market of Minneapolis to Chicago is 13.43 cents, which is

[10] This will be discussed in a later section of this chapter.

about 11 cents less than the transportation cost from Minnesota country points to Chicago. However, this proportional rate can only be used if there is a 9.9 cents-per-bushel inbound charge to apply to the movement of the grain out of Minneapolis.

Another qualification is that, in actual practice, the track bids made by the processor are not measured from each town in Minnesota. Usually blocks of towns in a fairly small area are combined and used to figure an average transportation cost for the region. This makes it easier to give buying price quotations to commission men, and it also widens the competitive area supplying the soybeans.

The selling process is also less exact than was evidenced by the specific examples. Average estimates of the location advantage of specific states, rather than towns, in shipping meal by freight are used (Table 35). Also an over-all average transportation advantage

TABLE 35. The Over-all Freight Advantages per Ton of Meal Shipped, as Used by Commercial Men for Territories Rather Than Specific Locations *

Areas	Amount of Advantage
Mankato, Minnesota	$6.00
State of Minnesota	4.25
Minneapolis, Minnesota	4.50
North Dakota	3.75
South Dakota	3.25
Montana	3.40
Wisconsin	3.10
Sioux City, Iowa †	3.00
Washington and Oregon	2.70
Idaho	2.40
California	1.35

* Data gathered from commercial sources.
† Freight break point.

on all meal sales is estimated for the year. The latter depends upon the size of the processing plant. If the processing plant is small and the processor can purchase soybeans directly from the farmer and sell meal directly to him, then the transportation advantage of this firm is as much as $10 a ton. On the other hand, if the processing plant requires large supplies of soybeans and wide market outlets, a processor is unable to buy a large proportion of his soybeans locally or sell a majority of the meal in his immediate area. In Minnesota such processors hope for a $3- to $4-per-ton transportation advantage.

The location disadvantage of selling oil from Minnesota was not brought out by the preceding examples. Since most of the oil markets are to the east and south of Minnesota, Minnesota processors have a transportation disadvantage of ⅛ to ¼ cent a pound.

Finally, the transportation advantage of meal as determined for the Mankato processor is not realistic. Usually Decatur-processed meal sells at a premium over western restricted meal and eastern restricted meal.[11] This disadvantage of restricted meal amounts to as much as $4 a ton, much of the transportation advantage of processing firms located in Minnesota thus being eliminated. The advantage, or lack of it, depends upon the local competitive situation. It is usually the last car of meal or soybeans sold and bought that sets the market for an area. For example, a Mankato processor may be willing to sell meal at a discount under the Decatur price to obtain the western market as long as he retains some of his local transportation advantage. But as he decreases his price, his competitors do likewise, and again his transportation advantage is narrowed. Another limitation of the transportation advantage of the Minnesota processor is the fact that he usually cannot afford to sell most of his meal on the spot market because most processors have to be sure of an outlet for the day-to-day production of soybean meal without having to worry about selling meal at distressed prices. The processor, therefore, usually sells most of his meal for nearby delivery-month shipments. This deferred market tends to give unrestricted meal a slight price advantage. As of this writing (March 1952), meal is in extremely short supply, so both restricted and unrestricted meal are selling at the ceiling price. Hence the Minnesota processor is able to realize the full freight saving when he sells to the local Minnesota market. The local buyers, however, may not want to buy when the local processor is producing, so that not all of the meal can be sold in the Minnesota market, even though it is an extremely good one.

[11] Restricted meal is that meal produced by a processor in a location far enough away from Decatur to permit advantageous sales in a local area; but, at the same time, this meal is sold at an advantage only in this restricted local area. The Decatur processed meal is considered unrestricted meal. Eastern restricted meal is produced by processing plants located to the east of Decatur. Mankato represents a location for western restricted meal in that the Minnesota processor's most advantageous sales are made within the state and to the states west of Minnesota.

Foreign market. The foreign market also affects the competitive position of the Minnesota soybean processor in that it offers an attractive market outlet for Minnesota soybean producers. Naturally, the processor will bid the price up to retain local supplies, but the foreign market presses him to do so. Transportation has also played an important role in the movement of Minnesota soybeans into the foreign market. As much as 20 per cent of the Minnesota soybean crop was exported in 1951. Part of the explanation of this movement is the transportation advantages of shipping soybeans to Canada, Japan, and Europe.

Soybeans were shipped from Minnesota to Japan over two different routes.[12] The main route was as follows: Duluth to Montreal; Montreal to the Atlantic; around the Panama Canal; and the Pacific Ocean to Japan. The following costs were incurred from the Minneapolis market:

5	cents a bushel railroad rate, Minneapolis to Duluth, plus an inbound freight rate of 7.2 cents a bushel from interior points to Minneapolis
3	cents a bushel elevator charge to Duluth
18	cents a bushel lake freight
2	cents a bushel loading steamer to Montreal
28	cents a bushel

The Chicago market is in a less favorable position to satisfy this Japanese demand. The Chicago market costs are as follows:

3	cents a bushel elevator cost at Chicago
16	cents a bushel freight cost by lake
2	cents a bushel loading steamers to Montreal
21	cents a bushel

There is an approximate 14 cents-a-bushel price differential between the Minneapolis and Chicago markets; therefore, the price of Minnesota soybeans at Montreal would be 14 cents over Chicago. The price of Chicago soybeans at Montreal, from the above computation, is 21 cents over Chicago, or an advantage of 7 cents a bushel in favor of the Minneapolis market.

The local processors allowed such a shipment of soybeans to leave Minnesota because crushing margins were low in the early part of 1951

[12] At the time soybeans were shipped to Japan, Minnesota was the only available source of supply, owing to ceiling prices. Exporters preferred to sell low oil content Minnesota soybeans and get extra profit by using round about transportation costs. The Japanese customers were so eager for the soybeans that they were willing to pay these costs.

and processors did not want to buy beans for processing plants that were not operating.[13] Minnesota beans normally would not be used for the export market because the railroad rates to the main export ports are very high. The rail rate from Minneapolis to Seattle is 61 cents a bushel; from Minneapolis to New Orleans, 30 cents a bushel; and from Minneapolis to Baltimore, 34 cents a bushel. But the export demand was extremely good, and the Mississippi and North Carolina soybean production was not enough to satisfy it. Minnesota soybeans were therefore in demand.

The future prospects of the export market for Minnesota soybeans is excellent in Canada because of that country's growing processing industry and the cheap water transportation available. Exports to Japan will probably fall off as it is not a normal soybean-trading country for the United States. Exporters are enthusiastic about the potential Minnesota soybean production as they feel that it could develop into a much more reliable source for exportable soybeans than the present production of the ocean states of North Carolina and Mississippi.[14]

SUMMARY

In summary, the Minnesota processor has three main transportation advantages. They are as follows:

(1) The most significant advantage is the excellent local meal market, which permits the charging of a Decatur price and allows the freight from Decatur to become part of the processor's profit.

(2) The second advantage is due to the Chicago basis of pricing soybeans. The Minnesota processor can usually buy his soybeans freight off the Chicago cash price whereas other processors in Illinois and Iowa have to pay more for their soybeans.

(3) The final advantage is the extremely low rail rates operative within Minnesota.

In order to take advantage of these favorable transportation rates the processor should have several railroads servicing him, to maximize transit privileges and to provide adequate flexibility, in order to maintain good bargaining power with the railroad.

The transportation disadvantages of the Minnesota location are also three in number, but are heavily outweighed by the above advantages. They are as follows:

[13] This situation will be discussed more fully in a later section of this chapter.
[14] Interview with James Mullin of Leval & Co. Inc.

(1) The lack of transit privileges for soybean oil and the fact that most oil is consumed in areas where Minnesota is at a competitive transportation disadvantage of ⅛ to ¼ cent a pound.

(2) The fact that the meal markets available to the Minnesota processor are limited to areas within the state and to the west and north of Minnesota.

(3) The importance of the export market for Minnesota. This is additional competition for the Minnesota processor.

To maximize the transportation advantages of the Minnesota location, adequate storage is a necessity for the processor. Therefore, the next factor affecting the competitive position of the Minnesota processor that merits analysis is storage.

STORAGE

The Minnesota processor's transportation advantage in selling meal and buying soybeans is in part dependent upon the storage facilities at the processing plant and on the farm. If a processor has facilities available to store soybean meal, he is in a better position to sell more of his meal in the local area, as he can satisfy these needs when the local purchasers decide to buy. However, the storage of meal is costly. Meal is difficult to handle and can deteriorate quickly. In addition, the local consumers will want meal when its cost is most advantageous to them and not to the processor. Only one processor in the state has facilities to store soybean meal. As these facilities are available for the storage of either soybeans or meal, the processor is in a flexible position to decide which storage policy will be most profitable to him. If storing soybean meal should become more profitable to this firm, others may build storage facilities and narrow this company's competitive advantage. The end result would be a more uniform supply of soybean meal that would be able to satisfy the seasonal needs of different types of livestock. At the present time (March 1952), the unprecedented demand for the immediate delivery of soybean meal makes it unlikely that any additional meal storage space will be built.

Most processors have storage facilities to accommodate from a third to a half of the soybeans they utilize each year. These facilities enable them to buy soybeans in the local area at harvest time or at other periods of crop movement and to maximize their transportation advantage. If these facilities were not there, many Minnesota soybean supplies would move to "deficit" producing states and to the export market. The processor needs soybean supplies the year around, and he would have to bid for them at higher levels to obtain them before or after major crop movements take place. In other words, buying soybeans under the Chicago cash price would become very difficult. In addition, the processor needs a large storage capacity to enable him to obtain as many "dry" soybeans as possible.[15] The present available storage space at processing plants seems adequate for the soybean crop (Table 36).

TABLE 36. Available Storage Space and Estimated Requirement for United States Soybean Mills, 1951–1952 Crush *

State	Space Available		Estimated Requirement, Tons
	Soybeans Only, Tons	All Oilseeds, Tons	
Arkansas	56,597	57,797	152,516
Illinois	830,848	1,161,498	762,286
Indiana	369,377	376,922	238,686
Iowa	317,719	456,543	233,602
Kansas	12,713	22,104	31,081
Kentucky	99,646	99,646	98,635
Minnesota	52,036	109,698	63,571
Missouri	93,418	197,394	124,006
Nebraska	....	23,377	26,924
North Carolina	37,100	37,100	53,105
Ohio	308,861	365,009	230,540
Total	2,178,315	2,907,088	2,014,952

* Source: Donald Jackson, "Storage Situation at Oil Mills," *Marketing Activities*, October 1951, p. 10.
The reporting mills in all states amounted to 85 per cent of all mills.

The processor's decision to build large storage facilities does not mean that he necessarily will be in an advantageous situation. The recent development of storage facilities on the farm affects the processor's decision. In the past, farmers marketed 75 per cent to 80 per cent of their soybean crop from October to December (Table 37). This enormous volume of selling at harvest time aggravated the seasonal box-car shortage. This market glut also resulted in congestion at country elevators, terminal markets, and processing plants, and led to seasonably low prices. The increasing soybean stocks on farms at the beginning of each year in recent years, indicate farmers have stored

[15] In the technical section, it was noted that beans high in moisture create costly processing problems.

TABLE 37. Monthly Sales of Soybeans by Farmers, as Percentage of Total Sales, in Ten Soybean-Producing States, Marketing Year, 1947–1948 *

State	1947				1948							
	Sept.	Oct.	Nov.	Dec.	Jan.	Feb.	Mar.	Apr.	May	June	July	Aug.
Arkansas	1	51	33	5	2	2	2	1	1	1	1	..
Illinois	2	57	15	6	7	2	1	2	3	3	1	1
Indiana	4	58	14	4	7	1	1	1	2	6	1	1
Kentucky	4	48	23	8	4	2	3	4	1	1	1	1
Michigan	1	55	14	5	7	2	1	4	4	5	2	..
Minnesota	1	53	14	5	12	2	2	3	3	3	1	1
Missouri	3	57	22	8	2	..	..	5	2	..	1	..
Nebraska	..	48	17	14	14	1	1	1	1	2	1	..
Ohio	2	55	16	6	7	1	2	2	4	4	1	..
South Dakota	1	52	13	5	5	1	2	9	4	4	4	..

* Source: D. B. Agnew and C. H. Keirstead, *Cash Costs of Farm Storage in Marketing Soybeans*, P.M.A., Fats and Oils Branch, U.S. Department of Agriculture, September 1950, p. 53.

TABLE 38. Soybean Stocks on Minnesota Farms, Quarterly, 1943–1952, by Thousand Bushels *

Quarter	1943	1944	1945	1946	1947	1948	1949	1950	1951	1952
January 1	2,378	1,548	961	1,311	2,455	3,312	4,840	4,722	8,897	8,105
April 1	1,278	791	721	983	1,601	2,484	3,904	3,318	4,096	....
July 1	426	362	260	131	427	276	781	319	492	....
October 1	177	132	80	98	107	207	234	64	164	....

* Source: Minnesota Agricultural Statistics, 1943–1952, State-Federal Crop and Livestock Reporting Service.

more soybeans (Appendix, Table 26).[16] In January 1951 Minnesota farmers held 55 per cent of the state's soybean crop and in January 1952, about 45 per cent (Table 38).[17] The encouragement of farm storage by the government, the higher income taxes that encourage some farmers to hold crops over the first of the year, together with the possibility of higher prices, have induced farmers to retain more of their soybean crop each year. As farmer holdings of soybeans increase each year, the processor's large storage facilities may become "white elephants."

Nevertheless, the processor still needs large storage facilities for soybeans. He is in the crushing business, and his problem is to buy his raw

[16] This is also due in part to larger soybean crops each year.

[17] The nation as a whole had a larger percentage of soybeans on the farm in 1952. But the moisture content of Minnesota beans was so high that many were unfit for storage.

material when it is obtainable, regardless of whether or not availability is at harvest time. In Chapter IV it was noted that the crushing capacity of the processing industry is greater than the crop produced. Therefore, it is the obtaining of the soybeans to run large-scale processing plants that is important to the processor, and he must have the facilities to buy and store the soybeans whenever they are available.

It may be to the producers' advantage as well as to the processors that more soybeans are stored at processing plants or at elevator locations than on the farm. If soybeans are stored for less than six months by the farmer, cost studies indicate that storage costs are higher on the farm than in elevators (Appendix, Table 27). In addition, price movements can be down as well as up, and it is to the farmer's advantage that processors and elevator operators have available storage capacity sufficient to purchase his crop.[18] Also, storage requires excellent know-how in the proper conditioning of the crop. Soybeans must be extremely dry and free from foreign material when stored; otherwise conditions for mold growth are prevalent. The loss due to poor conditioning in storage is both a shrinkage in the total weight and a price discount based on changes in various grade factors when the soybeans finally are marketed (Appendix, Table 28).

In summary, storage facilities do enable the processor in Minnesota to utilize the transportation advantage of the local supply of soybeans when they become available. Future meal storage facilities will be competitively important to the Minnesota processor if the market for meal should weaken and if definite seasonal demands occur.

Finally, storage, by itself, is neither profitable nor unprofitable for the producer, middleman, and processor. Its advantage depends on a changing price situation, transportational effects, and the knowledge and experience of each type of operator. It is obvious that the enormous crop movement during the harvest time coupled with inadequate storage and transportation facilities has contributed greatly to the sharp price fluctuations of the soybean crop, but this relation cannot be isolated as the only factor in such a price change.

In addition to affecting one another in relation to the competitive position of the Minnesota processor, the factors of transportation and storage also have an impact upon the relation between the processor and commodity markets.

[18] In the past, storage capacity has not been adequate, and many producers feel that by having their own storage, they can always be assured facilities.

COMMODITY MARKETS

The factors of transportation and storage both affect the influence of the commodity markets upon the competitive position of the Minnesota processor. It has been noted that the Minnesota processor must have adequate storage facilities in order to maximize his transportation advantage at the time of the Minnesota soybean crop movement. These large soybean inventories acquired by the Minnesota processor are subject to wide price swings (Tables 39 and 40). Some means is needed to reduce his inventory price risk and to retain his favorable soybean purchase-price advantage. The processor usually turns to hedging on the commodity markets for his protection against inventory price fluctuations.

TABLE 39. Range of Contract Cash Prices of Soybeans at Chicago, Monthly *

1950	Price per Bushel, Soybeans, No. 3 U.S. Yellow and Better	
	Low	High
January	$2.22	$2.34
February	2.18½	2.42¼
March	2.41¾	2.55
April	2.54	2.94½
May	2.85¾	3.22½
June	2.87½	3.15½
July	3.06¾	3.26½
August	2.62	2.92
September	2.67	2.67
October	2.15	2.67½
November	2.52¼	2.94
December	2.85½	3.18½
Range, 1950	$2.15	$3.26½

* The source of the data in this and the following table is the *Ninety-third Annual Report* of the Chicago Board of Trade.

Hedging is defined by the Chicago Board of Trade as follows: "A means of protection against inventory loss due to adverse price changes by simultaneously offsetting the purchase or sale of cash grain by counter-balancing the sale or purchase of an equivalent amount of futures." [19]

In order for the hedge to be completely effective in avoiding inventory risks, futures and cash prices must move up and down together,

[19] R. H. Moulton, *A Manual of Trading in Grain Futures and in Cash Grains on the Chicago Board of Trade.*

TABLE 40. Range of Contract Cash Prices of Soybeans at Chicago, Yearly

Year	Range for the Entire Year		Months the Lowest and Highest Prices Were Reached	
	Low	High	Lowest	Highest
1939	$0.80	$1.28½	Feb.	Dec.
1940	0.74¼	1.21	Oct.	Jan.
1941	0.91¼	1.94	Feb.	Sept.
1942	1.65¼	1.96¾	June	Feb.
1943	1.71¼	1.92	Mar. thru Oct.	Oct.
1944	1.86	2.17	Jan.	Sept.
1945	2.10	2.22	Oct.	Dec.
1946	2.22	3.51	Feb.	Oct.
1947	2.92	4.07	Sept.	Nov.
1948	2.35¼	4.43	Oct.	Jan.
1949	2.12	3.20	Oct., Nov.	Aug.
1950	2.15	3.26½	Oct.	July

and the value of the meal and oil must determine the price of soybeans. In practice, neither of these conditions is present in stable relationships. However, the fact that futures and cash prices tend to move together and that the price of soybeans tends to be determined by the price of meal and oil give the processor the opportunity of hedging in the commodity markets, but do not guarantee that his inventories will not be affected by price fluctuations.

The Minnesota processor has many commodity markets available to him. The Chicago futures market for soybeans, meal, and oil; the Chicago and Minneapolis cash soybean markets; the futures oil market of New York; and the futures meal market of Memphis. The market most frequently used by the Minnesota processor is that of Chicago. He utilizes the Chicago cash market in determining his purchase bids to Minnesota farmers;[20] therefore, it is natural that the soybean, meal, and oil futures markets of Chicago are used for his hedging operations. The only futures market for soybeans is located in Chicago.

Most of the time the relation of the cash market to the futures market for soybeans permits favorable hedging opportunities to the Minnesota processor (Fig. 32).[21] However, "squeezes" can occur in certain future

[20] As indicated early in the transportation section of this study.

[21] Favorable opportunities in the sense that a carrying charge is evident in the nearby future month which narrows down toward the end of the time this month is used for hedging. This situation indicates a normal decrease in storage and risk charges as the time of the future contract decreases. Futures delivery months for soybeans are January, March, May, July, September, and November.

FIGURE 32. Prices of Soybeans: Cash Prices of Number 2 Yellow at Minneapolis, on Track Bids at Minnesota Country Points; and Futures Prices at Chicago, 1950.

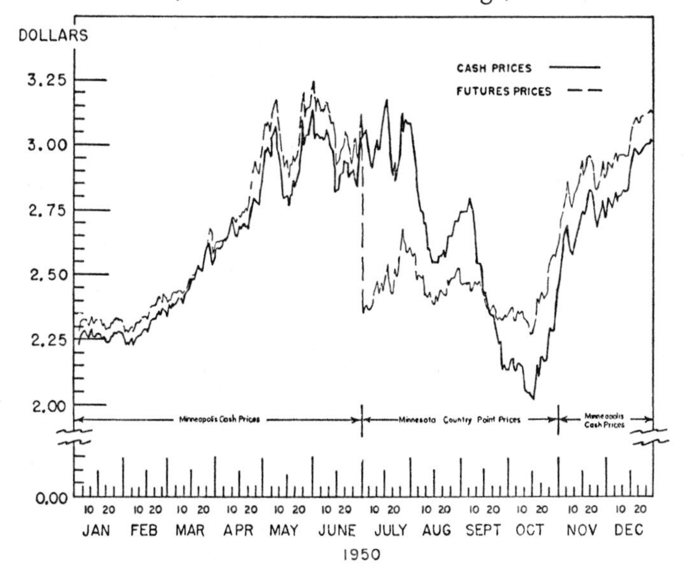

delivery months if the "shorts" in the market cannot cover their position with the actual cash commodity.[22] In May of 1950 such a "squeeze" took place (Fig. 32). The possibility of such "squeezes" taking place on the Chicago market is greater today than in the past because of the decreasing amount of soybeans actually shipped to the Chicago market (Table 41). This situation could be alleviated by the use of multiple delivery points. Such points should be located in such a way as to take advantage of the normal movement of the crop – e.g., Decatur.[23] This decrease in cash soybean supplies in Chicago which leads to possible "squeezes" on the Chicago soybean market was further aggravated in 1951 when ceiling prices were operative. The ceiling prices between the Chicago cash market and country-point price of Illinois, Iowa, and Minnesota were less than the full freight differentials. In consequence, soybeans located at Chicago were cheaper than those located in other positions, which meant that in the movement of the soybean crop, sup-

[22] It is true that less than 1 per cent of all futures contracts are filled by the actual delivery of grain. The importance of having grain available in the terminal market is due to the ever present alternative to accept or to deliver the commodity in fulfillment of the contract.

[23] Multiple delivery points are used for the meal and oil futures markets.

TABLE 41. Receipts of Soybeans at Chicago and Minneapolis Grain Centers for the Last Five Years [*]

Year	Number of Bushels	
	Chicago	Minneapolis
1946	17,118,000	9,515,000
1947	13,923,000	5,700,000
1948	14,616,000	7,203,000
1949	19,119,000	5,717,000
1950	19,492,000	3,596,000

[*] Source: *Sixty-eighth Annual Report* of the Minneapolis Grain Exchange, and *Ninety-third Annual Report* of the Chicago Board of Trade.

plies would tend to avoid the Chicago market. Those supplies already in Chicago would be used more rapidly.

The effect of such possible Chicago market "squeezes," as indicated above, is especially important to the Minnesota processor. The fluctuating relationship between the cash prices of soybeans in the Minneapolis and Chicago markets in 1950 indicates that the full transportation differential between the Minneapolis and Chicago soybean markets of 13.41 cents a bushel is seldom reached (Fig. 33). In addition to indicating a strong local processing demand for Minnesota soybeans, this price relationship also illustrates that if a Minnesota processor is caught in a "squeeze" by hedging in the Chicago market, he will either have to deliver soybeans to Chicago at a full freight cost (a charge he was unable to obtain from the farmer when he purchased his local soybeans) or he will have to buy back his contract with the same additional loss involved. In other words, if the Minneapolis price was 5 cents under the Chicago price and a market squeeze forced a processor to deliver soybeans to Chicago at 13.41 cents, he would lose 8.41 cents a bushel in the transaction. The Illinois processors are in more advantageous positions if a "squeeze" develops, as they are closer to the Chicago market; and transportation price differentials and actual market price variations are more in line with each other.[24]

Another inadequacy of the Chicago market for hedging transactions, but one that is equally applicable to all processors, is the change from "old" to "new" crop tradings. As the July delivery month comes to a

[24] The same is not true for Iowa; for historically Minnesota soybeans are more likely to be delivered on the Chicago market because of their low oil content, even though they are located further away from the Chicago market than are the Iowa soybeans.

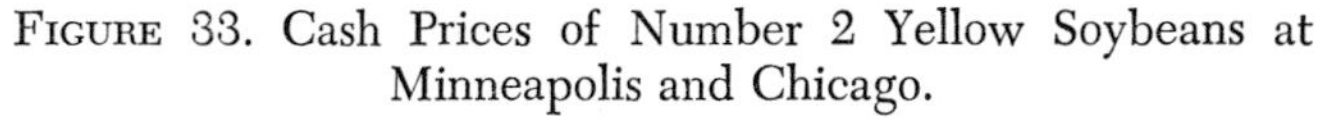

FIGURE 33. Cash Prices of Number 2 Yellow Soybeans at Minneapolis and Chicago.

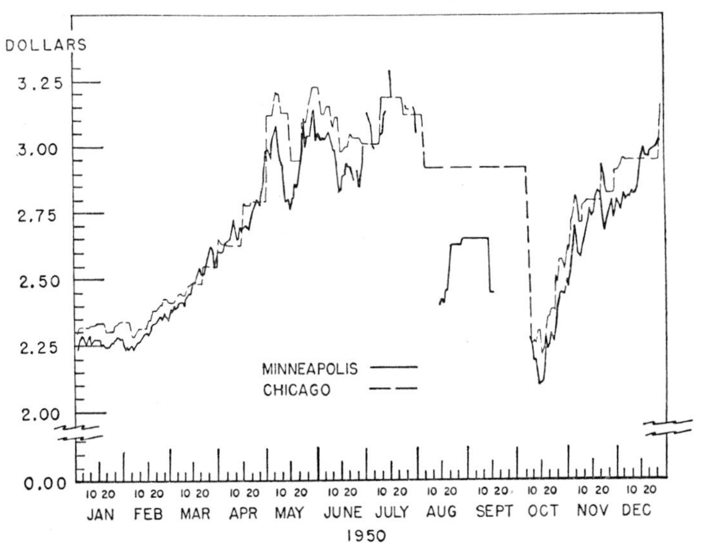

close, many hedges have to be placed in the September or November trading months. Transactions in these future months have already discounted the new crop, whereas the cash market is still based on the old crop. In consequence, there is a wide inverse relationship between the cash and future markets until the new crop is harvested in October and November (Fig. 32). Therefore, from July to October, Minnesota and other processors do not have an adequate commodity market in which to hedge their soybean purchases. Not very many purchases, however, are made in these months.

Inventory policies of Minnesota processors and the use or non-use of the commodity markets are similar to the policies of the processors in other states. Some processors speculate in that they become "long" the future option as well as being "long" their inventories. Others attempt to hedge by keeping cash purchases of soybeans in line with cash sales of meal and oil; or they are long the "option" and short cash sales; or they use any number of combinations of futures market operations in arriving at a satisfactory hedge. The Minnesota processor, because of his location, is especially interested in the transportation differentials compared with the actual differentials among commodity markets. He is constantly buying back contracts in one market and selling them in another. Or if he is part of a well-integrated company, he exchanges contracts with his company's processing plants in other parts of the country. If a processor is not part of a large organization, he may exchange contracts with his competitors to the mutual advantage of both if the product qualities are the same. This constant inventory shifting to take advantage of transportation positions requires a flexible hedging policy for the Minnesota processor.

The factors of transportation, storage, and commodity markets are important aids in the understanding of the Minnesota processor's position in price formulation.

PRICE FORMULATION

Prices are extremely important in any economic system. They act as signals and results of the various aspects of supply and demand. Before we examine the specific position of the Minnesota processor in price formulation, a general description of the factors determining prices in this industry is needed. Such factors include the following: the production of soybeans and other protein and vegetable oil crops, and their competitive position in areas suitable to their growth, as outlined in Chapter II; the utilization of the processed products of oil and meal and their respective competitors in such utilization, as outlined in Chapter III; the processing industry's technological development and costs, as outlined in Chapter IV; and the transportation, storage, and commodity market factors that affect these supply and demand elements in the various market localities. In addition to these elements in the formulation of prices in the soybean industry, government action affecting all of these factors cannot be overlooked.

GOVERNMENT ACTION

The first government action affecting the soybean price structure was the enactment of a tariff in 1930 on soybeans, oil, and meal. This encouraged the development of the industry in the United States, but had no particular area effect.

The next government action affecting the soybean industry took place during World War II. These actions included the maintaining of high supports for livestock and livestock products, which anticipated heavier consumer demands for meat, which in turn meant more demands for soybean meal. Cotton acreage was decreased, the chief competition of soybean oil thus being limited. The increase of soybean

TABLE 42. Price Supports, Price Ceilings, and Average Prices Received by Farmers for Soybeans, Crop Years 1940–1951 *

Item	Dollars per Bushel of Soybeans
Average price received	
1940	0.90
1941	1.55
1942	
Support price	1.60
Ceiling price	1.66
Average price received	1.61
1943	
Support price	1.80
Ceiling price	1.92
Average price received	1.82
1944	
Support price	2.04
Ceiling price	2.10
Average price received	2.05
1945	
Support price	2.04
Ceiling price	2.10
Average price received	2.08
1946	
Support price	2.04
Ceiling price	...
Average price received	2.57
Average price received	
1947	
Support price	2.04
Ceiling price	...
Average price received	3.34
1948	
Support price	2.18
Ceiling price	...
Average price received	2.27
1949	
Support price	2.11
Ceiling price	...
Average price received	2.16
1950	
Support price	2.06
Ceiling price	...
Average price received	2.32
1951	
Support price	2.45
Ceiling price	3.06†
Average price received	3.08‡

* Source: P.M.A., Fats and Oils Division, and B.A.E., U.S. Department of Agriculture.
† Legal minimum for ceiling prices in the country, February 15, 1951.
‡ Average, February 15, 1951.

acreage was encouraged by high support prices (Table 42). During the war soybean supports were higher than ceiling prices of meal and oil. At this time the government paid the extra cost of the processor's soybeans in order that the processor would be certain of an adequate crushing margin. These actions did not affect the Minnesota processor's competitive advantage.

Supports for soybeans were continued after the war (Table 41). However, the market price remained higher than the support price. In consequence, very few soybeans were purchased by the Commodity Credit Corporation. The largest percentage of the crop to be under price-support programs was 7 per cent in 1949. In 1950 only 5 per cent of the crop was under price-support programs (Fig. 34). These ac-

FIGURE 34. Soybeans under Price Support Programs, United States, 1941–1950.

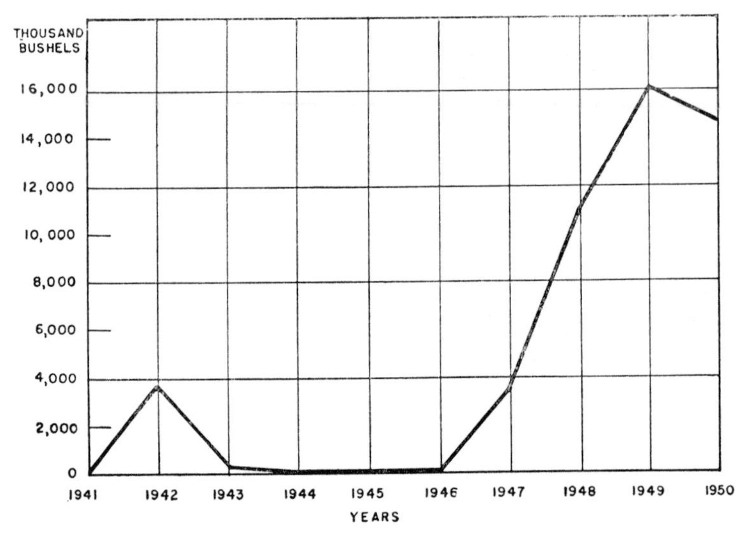

tions, again, did not affect the Minnesota processor in any unique manner.

The ceiling prices that became effective February 12, 1951, for soybeans, oil, and meal did have a direct bearing upon the competitive position of the Minnesota processor. The "normal" soybean transportation cost differential between Minnesota country-point stations and Illinois country-point stations is approximately 12 cents a bushel. This differential, in practice, fluctuates rather widely (Fig. 35). One of the reasons for such fluctuation is the difference in harvest time among Illinois, Iowa, and Minnesota producers. Because Illinois and Iowa processors have access to soybeans before Minnesota processors, the latter tend to bid up the price to obtain the first Minnesota soybeans in order to begin crushing early enough to meet some of their September and October meal and oil contracts (Fig. 35). In consequence, Minnesota soybean prices during August and September may be above those of Illinois and Iowa (Figs. 35 and 36). Other factors such as an over response to a market "squeeze" in Chicago may move too many soybeans from Minnesota to cover contracts, and leave supplies too short for the processing capacity in the state. Also, special efforts by some traders to depress the Illinois market may occur (Fig. 35).

FIGURE 35. Prices of Soybeans: On Track Bids at Minnesota and Illinois Country Points.

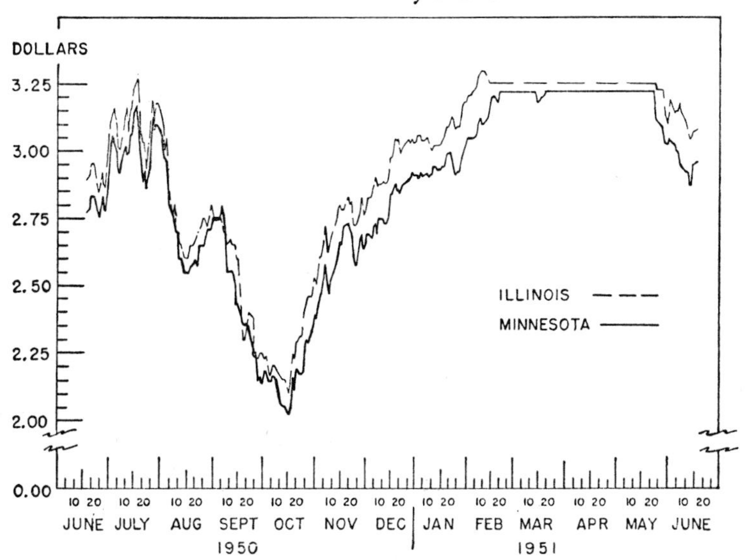

FIGURE 36. Prices of Soybeans: On Track Bids at Minnesota and Iowa Country Points.

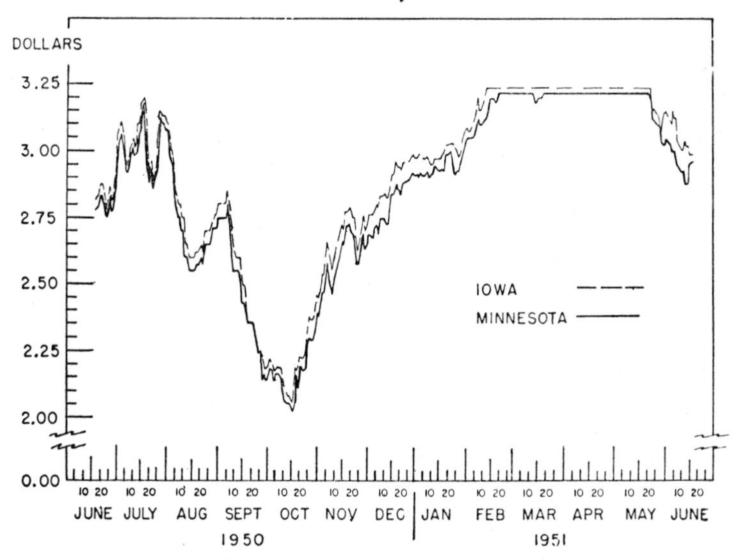

But even though the above conditions distort the normal transportation differential between Illinois and Minnesota, this differential usually is operative throughout most of the trading year and during the major movements of the crop (Fig. 35). The transportation cost differential of 12 cents a bushel between Illinois country points and Minnesota country points was not taken into full consideration in the establishment of ceiling prices. The government set this price differential at 3 cents a bushel. Consequently, when ceiling prices became operative, the Minnesota processor's maximum advantage in purchasing soybeans within his state was decreased 9 cents a bushel (Fig. 35). The same situation was true of the relation between the Iowa and Minnesota processor. The "normal" transportation difference of 5 cents a bushel was reduced to 2 cents a bushel. In consequence, when ceiling prices were in effect, the competitive advantage of the Minnesota processor's position relative to that of the Illinois and Iowa processor was reduced. However, one Minnesota processor, when asked how he would set soybean ceiling price differentials, answered, "Probably in the same manner as the government so as not to penalize the Minnesota soybean producer by freezing his price at the full transportation cost differential between Illinois and Minnesota country points."

In certain respects, however, the application of ceiling prices affects all processors to practically the same degree; that is, the disadvantage experienced by the Minnesota processor is not very different from that of the Illinois and Iowa processor. The ceiling price relationships in Illinois illustrate some of the processor's problems: soybeans at country track stations in Illinois have a ceiling price of $3.23 a bushel; soybean oil, basis Decatur, has a ceiling price of 20½ cents a pound; and meal, basis Decatur, a price of $74 a ton (Tables 43 and 44). In effect, this means that if all three items were at ceiling prices, the processor would have a crushing margin of 56 cents a bushel. This margin is more than adequate to cover processing costs and insure a processing profit. But in the early months of 1952, soybean meal has remained at the ceiling price, oil prices have dropped to less than 50 per cent of the ceiling price, and soybean prices have remained relatively high. The result is a crushing margin that is below many processors' variable costs.

The processor has two alternatives, either to shut down his plant, or find some way to get an additional price for his meal in the extremely short protein market. The methods used to obtain an adequate crush-

TABLE 43. Country Elevator Base Ceiling Prices for No. 1 and No. 2 Yellow and Green Soybeans *

State	Dollars per Bushel	State	Dollars per Bushel
Illinois	3.23	Missouri	3.21
Indiana	3.22	Nebraska	3.21
Iowa	3.22	Ohio	3.22
Kansas	3.21	South Dakota	3.20
Kentucky	3.20	Tennessee	3.20
Michigan	3.21	Wisconsin	3.21
Minnesota	3.20	Other States †	3.18

* Source: O.P.S. Taken from Supplement 3 to GCPR, effective February 12, 1951. Ceilings for black, brown, and mixed soybeans are 25 cents less.
† New York, New Jersey, Pennsylvania, North Dakota, Delaware, Maryland, Virginia, West Virginia, North and South Carolina, Georgia, Alabama, Mississippi, Arkansas, Louisiana, and Oklahoma.

TABLE 44. Ceiling Prices for Crude Soybean Oil, in Tank Cars, in Cents per Pound *

Location	f.o.b.	Location	Decatur, Ill. †
California, Oregon, Washington	21⅝	Delaware, Indiana, Kentucky, Michigan, New Jersey, New York, North Carolina, Ohio, Pennsylvania, South Carolina, Virginia, Wisconsin	20½
Arizona	21⅛		
Alabama, Arkansas, Florida, Georgia, Illinois, Kansas, Louisiana, Mississippi, Missouri, New Mexico, Oklahoma, Tennessee, Texas	20½		
Iowa, Minnesota, Nebraska, North Dakota, South Dakota	20⅜		

* Source: O.P.S. Taken from CPR 6, as amended.
† Plus freight to New York, minus freight from point of sale to New York City, but in no case is the ceiling less than 20½ cents.

ing margin include the following: custom crushing for mixed feed manufacturers, barter arrangements with farmers whereby meal is exchanged for soybeans, and mineralizing the meal.[25] The last, "adulterated meal," has been the chief method the processor has used in obtaining an adequate crushing margin. Those processors who are inte-

[25] Mineralizing includes adding mineral to the soybean meal, thereby changing the product enough to charge a higher price. The protein content is reduced by the addition of the mineral. Hence it is really an inferior product selling at a higher price.

grated are also forced to "mineralize" the meal they use in their own mixed-feed products. The ceiling price of mixed feeds is determined by the cost of the ingredients. Therefore, if competitors use mineralized feeds in their products and charge higher prices for their mixed feeds, then integrated companies will have to do the same in order to maximize the profits of their firms.

THE MINNESOTA PROCESSOR

The Minnesota processor's position in price formulation is fairly strong in the absence of government price regulations. The three main processing plants within the state generally "bid" the price for the area, as they are the chief market for the state's soybeans. The Minnesota processors are in an excellent competitive position because of the surplus of soybeans within the state compared with the crushing capacity. In addition, the small number of major processors within the state permits easy access to accurate information concerning each other's competitive actions. Because these firms usually set the tone of the Minnesota market, the psychology of the soybean buyers in these firms has a great deal to do with the day-to-day state price-fluctuations, even though supply and demand are the long-run price determinants.

Many times the Minnesota processor is not the major influence in the state's soybean market. It is possible for speculative operations, holdings by the farmer, governmental pronouncements, export requirements, and the crushing needs of other states to dictate the trend of the market. The processor then decides whether or not the crushing margin and processing-plant costs justify his following the price trend. If they do not, he will cease operations until a profitable crushing margin occurs.

In summary, the main interest of the Minnesota processor in price formulation is not the level of prices but rather the width of his crushing margin as determined by changing supply-and-demand factors, transportation differentials, and technological innovations.

CRUSHING MARGINS

The competitive position of the Minnesota processor in the soybean industry can best be measured by his crushing margin[26] compared with the crushing margins of processors in the two most important

[26] The difference between the price the processor pays for his soybeans and the price he receives for his meal and oil.

processing states — namely, Illinois and Iowa. Cost differences for individual firms in these states will also affect the competitive position of the Minnesota processor. The over-all, weighted processing cost of Minnesota firms compares fairly closely with the general operating costs of processors in other areas;[27] therefore, the analysis of crushing margin relationships remains the chief criterion in determining the competitive advantage of the Minnesota processor.

The variations in the crushing margins for Minnesota, Illinois, and Iowa processors are determined by differences in oil and meal yields and changes in the prices of soybeans, meal, and oil.

SPECIFIC EXAMPLE

The oil yields per bushel of soybeans produced and processed in Minnesota is one pound less than those produced and processed in Illinois and one half pound less than those produced and processed in Iowa. The degree of disadvantage depends upon the price of oil. The lower the price of oil, the less the Minnesota disadvantage. On December 28, 1951, the price of soybean oil was 12 cents a pound (Table 45). Therefore, at this time, the Illinois processor's oil-yield advantage over the Minnesota processor was 12 cents a bushel. The Iowa processor's advantage was 6 cents a bushel (Table 45).

The change in oil yields per bushel of soybeans processed naturally results in a similar volume change in the meal yields. Therefore, depending upon the price of meal, part of the Minnesota oil disadvantage is reduced. As of December 28, 1951, the price of meal was $74 a ton, or 3.7 cents a pound. In consequence, the Minnesota processor's advantage in his sale of meal is 3.7 cents a bushel with respect to Illinois processors and 1.85 cents a bushel with respect to Iowa processors.

The price of soybean oil f.o.b. Decatur, December 28, 1951, was 12 cents a pound (Table 45). The over-all freight disadvantage in shipping oil from Minnesota to points in the East competitive to the Decatur location is approximately 0.23 cents a pound. The disadvantage of the Minnesota location compared with that of Iowa for this factor is even less, amounting to 0.11 cents a pound.

The price of soybean meal f.o.b. Decatur, December 28, 1951, was $74 a ton. There was no discount for western restricted meal; so the Iowa and Minnesota prices were based upon the $74-a-ton price plus

[27] Chapter IV discusses processing costs.

TABLE 45. Estimated Differences in Crushing Margins among Illinois, Iowa, and Minnesota Processing Plants

	Solvent Method			Expeller Method		
	Illinois	Iowa	Minnesota	Illinois	Iowa	Minnesota
Oil yield per bushel	10.5 lbs.	10.0 lbs.	9.5 lbs.	9.0 lbs.	8.5 lbs.	8.0 lbs.
Meal yield per bushel	48.0 lbs.	48.5 lbs.	49.0 lbs.	49.5 lbs.	50.0 lbs.	50.5 lbs.
Waste per bushel	1.5 lbs.	1.5 lbs.	1.5 lbs.	1.5 lbs.	1.5 lbs.	1.5 lbs.
Price of oil *	12.0¢	11.88¢	11.77¢	12.0¢	11.88¢	11.77¢
Price of meal †	$74.00	$74.00	$74.00	$74.00	$74.00	$74.00
Freight pickup ‡	None	$ 2.00	$ 4.00	None	$ 2.00	$ 4.00
Oil recovery §	$ 1.26	$ 1.19	$ 1.12	$ 1.08	$ 1.01	$ 0.94
Meal recovery plus freight **	1.78	1.84	1.91	1.84	1.90	1.97
Total recovery ††	$ 3.04	$ 3.03	$ 3.03	$ 2.92	$ 2.91	$ 2.91
Less bean price ‡‡	2.87	2.78	2.73	2.87	2.78	2.73
Crushing margin	$ 0.17	$ 0.25	$ 0.30	$ 0.05	$ 0.13	$ 0.18

* Crude oil price, basis f.o.b. Decatur, December 28, 1951, 12 cents a pound. Freight disadvantage of 0.12 cents for Iowa and 0.23 cents for Minnesota location.

† $74 per ton ceiling f.o.b. Decatur. No western restricted discount at this time because of tight supply of meal. December 28, 1951.

‡ $4 average freight advantage of Minnesota location and $2 average freight advantage of Iowa location because of Decatur pricing basing system. (See previous section on transportation in this chapter.)

§ Price per pound × yield per bushel.

** Price per pound + freight pickup per pound × yield per bushel.

†† Per bushel basis.

‡‡ Prices of beans were based on the January futures price of Chicago less country-point transportation charges of 12 cents for Illinois, 20 cents for Iowa, and 24 cents for Minnesota. Price premiums for higher-oil-content beans in Illinois and Iowa were figured at 2 cents a bushel for Illinois and 1 cent for Iowa. All prices were obtained from the Wall Street Journal of December 29, 1951.

the freight advantage of selling meal in the local market. This advantage was figured conservatively at $4 a ton for the Minnesota location and $2 a ton for the Iowa location.

The variation in prices paid for soybeans among these three states is primarily dependent upon transportation differentials and slightly upon oil premiums. The prices for December 28, 1951, were based on the Chicago January futures price of $2.97 a bushel less freight to the country points plus the oil premiums of different locations. The freight costs to the Chicago market were figured as 12 cents a bushel for central Illinois, 20 cents for Iowa, and 24 cents for Minnesota. A 2-cent-per-bushel premium was paid in Illinois and a 1-cent-per-bushel premium in Iowa. The net effect is a purchase-price saving for Minnesota processors over those in Illinois of 14 cents a bushel and over those in Iowa of 4 cents a bushel.

From the above, it is obvious that the freight advantage of buying Minnesota beans on the basis of 24 cents a bushel under the Chicago option and selling meal on a Decatur-plus-freight basis of $4 a ton place the Minnesota processor in the best competitive position in the soybean industry.[28]

The disadvantage of the low oil-content of Minnesota soybeans, the additional freight cost in shipping oil, and possible discounts in the restricted meal market tend to decrease the extent of the advantage of the Minnesota location. But even with these disadvantages, the Minnesota processor's competitive position is evidenced in this specific example by his 13-cents-a-bushel crushing-margin advantage over the Illinois processor and his 5-cents-a-bushel crushing margin advantage over the Iowa processor (Table 45). The Minnesota competitive advantage exists in both the comparisons among solvent processing plants and among expeller processing plants (Table 45).

The preceding example, used to illustrate the strong competitive position of the Minnesota processor, has several limitations. In the first place, figures for waste, oil yields, and meal yields are based on state averages rather than on data for each particular firm. Waste is not a uniform amount for each firm, as it varies according to the capacity of the plant and the ability of the management. Oil and meal yields depend upon the type of machinery used, the skill of the labor involved, and the moisture content of the soybeans.

[28] This competitive position is limited to the three states under discussion. Areas in the South that grow soybeans and have excellent meal markets also are in a strong competitive position within the industry.

Transportation advantages were also based on average figures. The fact that a processing cost of 54 cents a bushel can exist for one firm and a cost of 20 cents for another suggests wide differences in the transportation advantages of individual firms to enable both firms to operate at a profit. For example, a small local processor can save as much as 10 cents a bushel[29] by purchasing his soybeans directly from the farmer, and he can add an additional 15-cents-a-bushel profit by disposing of all his meal at the maximum freight saving of $10 a ton rather than at the average of $4 a ton (Table 45). The saving of the small firm of 25 cents a bushel over the large processing plant almost covers the increased cost involved in operating the small mill in Minnesota.

FIGURE 37. Solvent Crushing Margins Compared to Weighted Processing Cost, Seven Minnesota Firms.

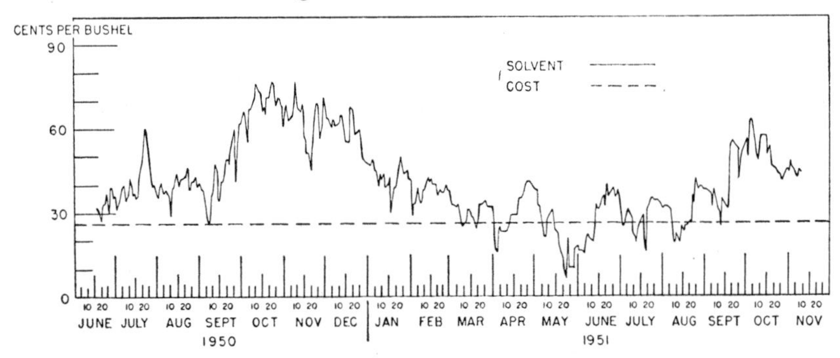

Disregarding the above limitations in the use of averages, the comparison of the past solvent crushing margins to the weighted average cost of seven Minnesota processing firms indicates that, in addition to being in a good competitive position, Minnesota processors have had fairly profitable operations (Fig. 37). In the late months of 1951 and in the early months of 1952, the decline in the price of oil has decreased these crushing margins to below the state's total weighted processing costs. But even during adverse times for the processing industry, Minnesota's strong competitive position results in less hardship for Minnesota processors and indicates that these processing plants would probably be the last to cease operations.

[29] This was illustrated in Chapter IV.

CRUSHING-MARGIN RELATIONSHIPS OVER TIME

Thus far the competitive position of the Minnesota processor has been determined by an analysis of the crushing-margin differentials among Illinois, Iowa, and Minnesota processors for a particular day. This was done to illustrate the specific effect of supply, demand, technological, and transportational factors upon the crushing margins of the processors in the three states. As these factors are constantly changing, the crushing-margin relationships among the processors of these states are also fluctuating, and in turn indicate changing competitive positions (Figs. 38, 39, 40, 41, and 42). Therefore, a more realistic appraisal of the competitive position of the Minnesota processor in the industry requires an analysis of crushing margins over time.

An analysis of these fluctuating crushing margins from June 17, 1950, to November 8, 1951, can best be undertaken by an examination of three specific periods: June 17, 1950 to November 15, 1950; November 15, 1950 to May 1951; and May 1951 to November 1951.

From June 17, 1950 to November 15, 1950, the crushing margin of the Minnesota location was in its most favorable position relative to the crushing margins for Illinois and Iowa (Figs. 39 and 40). The Korean War caused an overbuying in the soybean meal market. Western restricted meal was not being sold at a discount; therefore, the maximum transportation advantage could be obtained by the Minnesota processor. In addition, soybeans were plentiful, and the full freight rate from Chicago to the point of purchase could be deducted. Furthermore, processors were not aware of any lack of oil content in Minnesota soybeans and did not take this into account in their crushing-margin analysis.

From November 15, 1950 to May 1951 the Minnesota processor lost his competitive advantage in the soybean industry; and, in fact, was at a competitive disadvantage for most of this period. In November the processors in Minnesota realized that they had overestimated the oil content of Minnesota soybeans. In addition, a market reaction to peace rumors in Korea, together with a seasonal slump in the meal market, caused western restricted meal to sell at a discount. In consequence, the meal transportation advantage of the Minnesota processor was decreased. The final adverse effect occurred when government ceiling prices became operative in Minnesota on February 20, 1951. On February 10, 1951, the country-point track bids in Minnesota were 20 cents

FIGURE 38. Soybean Crushing Margins for Solvent and Expeller Plants in Minnesota.

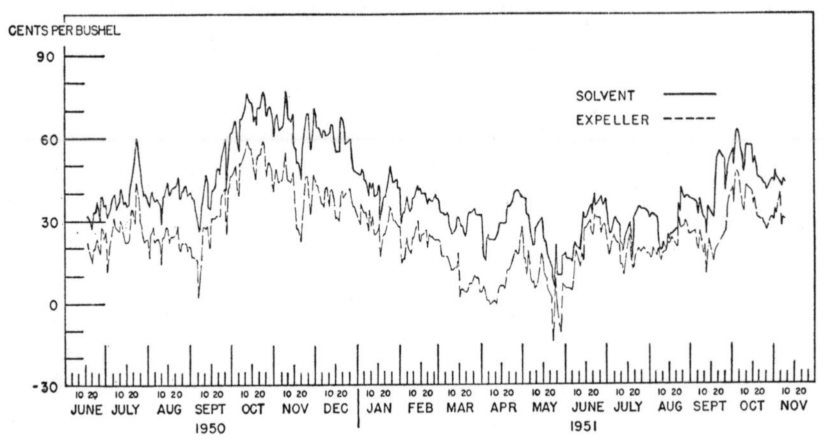

FIGURE 39. Soybean Crushing Margins for Solvent Plants in Minnesota and Illinois.

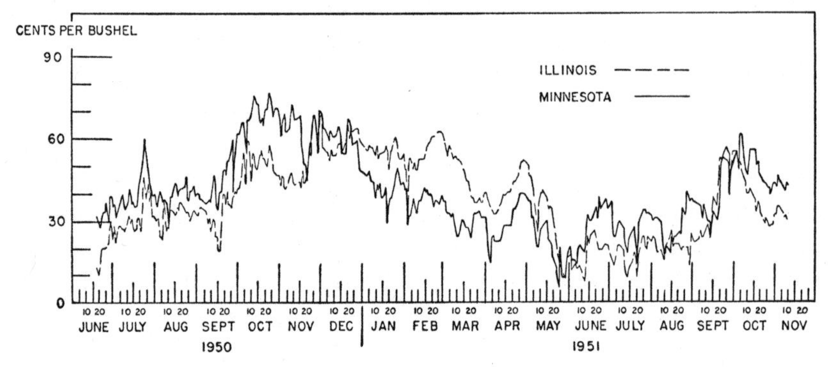

FIGURE 40. Soybean Crushing Margins for Solvent Plants in Minnesota and Iowa.

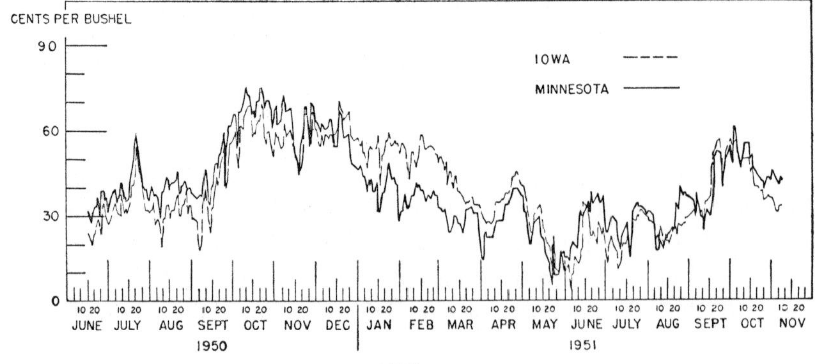

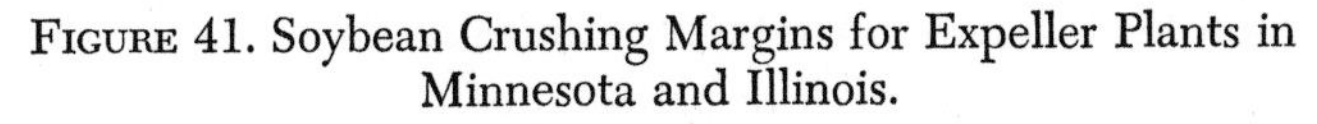

FIGURE 41. Soybean Crushing Margins for Expeller Plants in Minnesota and Illinois.

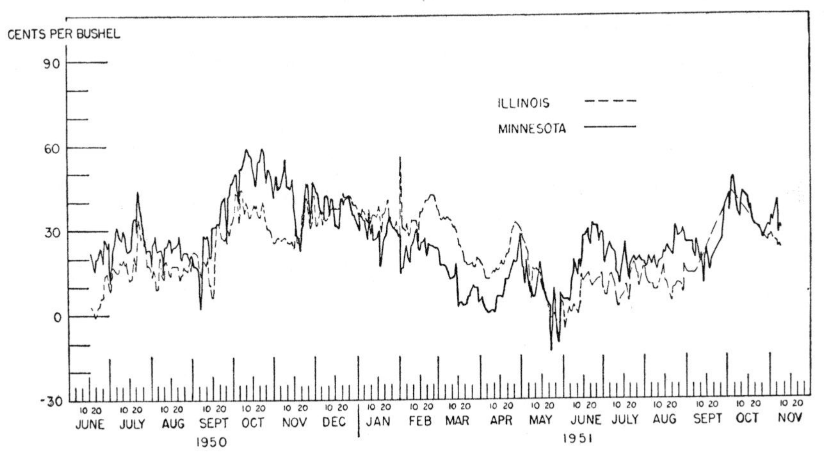

FIGURE 42. Soybean Crushing Margins for Expeller Plants in Minnesota and Iowa.

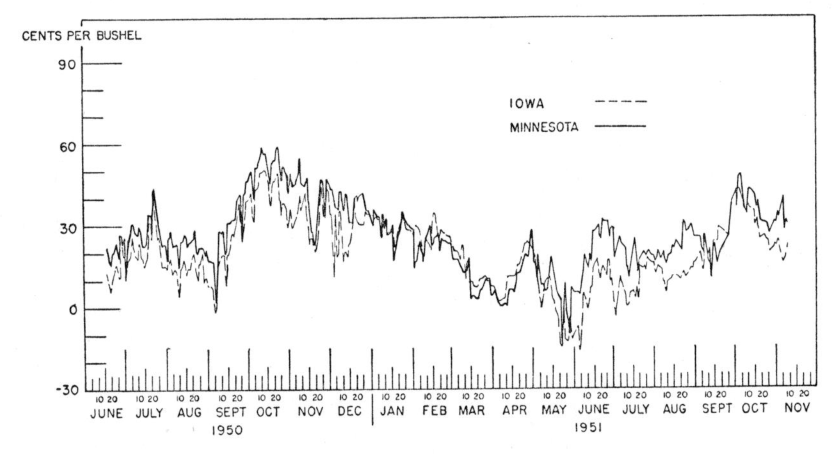

lower than those in Illinois. On February 20, 1951, the ceiling price differential was 3 cents a bushel. Hence, ceiling prices decreased the transportation advantage of the Minnesota processor in the purchase of his soybeans. In March the meal market recovered some strength, and in May soybeans fell from the ceiling price; the Minnesota processor was thus enabled to regain his competitive advantage.

From May 1951 to November 1951 the Minnesota processor was able to maintain his location advantage because of the presence of a strong meal market and the absence of artificial ceiling-price relationships between marketing areas.

The above analysis indicates that the Minnesota processor can maintain his competitive advantage in the soybean industry only if five conditions are fulfilled: (1) if the economics of the industry permit the continued use of a Decatur plus freight price for Minnesota meal and a Chicago less freight price for Minnesota soybeans; (2) if a strong local and western meal market exists; (3) if soybean supplies are plentiful in the state; (4) if government price relationships are not set so as to destroy the Minnesota processor's transportation advantages; and (5) if technological processing progress within the state keeps pace with national advances.

The Decatur and Chicago locations have been used as the price basis for the soybean industry during its rapid development. Therefore, any alteration in the use of these two locations would affect too many segments of this established industry to be feasible.

The analysis of the meal and livestock market in Chapter III indicates that Minnesota should continue to be a strong outlet for the processor's meal production. The Minnesota processing industry has yet to produce all the meal consumed in the state.

The supply of soybeans in Minnesota also seems plentiful, as the state's production is almost twice the processing capacity. In addition, the strong competitive position of the Minnesota processing industry assures the producer of an excellent market. The processing industry of Iowa and the export market of Canada are additional outlets for Minnesota soybean production. These markets should encourage continued production in the state. Furthermore, the comparative advantage of producing soybeans in the state is higher than that of any other crop with the exception of corn. Finally, the development within the state of soybean varieties with a higher oil content should increase even further the competitive position of the Minnesota processor.

Price ceilings on soybeans seem improbable in the near future as the weak oil market will tend to keep soybean prices at lower levels. Therefore, the danger of unrealistic price differentials coming into effect seems remote.

Finally, the Minnesota processing industry is a fairly efficient one. The main processing plants are large-scale, efficient, hexane-solvent operations. Many of them are flexible and have equipment to crush more than one type of oilseed crop. The major mills, moreover, are owned by nationally integrated firms that have their own markets for the meal and oil they process.

In conclusion, essential factors needed to insure a continuation of the strong competitive position of the Minnesota processing industry are present today and will be for some time in the foreseeable future. It is therefore safe to conclude this chapter by stating that the Minnesota processor, by virtue of his excellent local meal market, his large available supply of soybeans, and his favorable transportation location, is in a better competitive position in the soybean industry than are processors in any of the other main processing states.

CHAPTER VI

Summary and Conclusions

THE competitive position of the Minnesota soybean producer and processor is in part determined by the international and national factors of production, utilization, and processing that affect the soybean industry in America generally, and in part by the elements of transportation, storage, commodity markets, and price formulation which have a more direct bearing upon the advantages and disadvantages of the Minnesota location.

THE PRODUCER

The rapid development of the soybean crop in the United States during the last decade has enabled this country to become the world's leading producer of soybeans. Several interdependent elements of production and utilization have brought about this marked expansion of the crop. In the first place, the farmer's comparative advantage of growing soybeans in the suitable production area of the Corn Belt was immeasurably raised by the decreased soybean production in Asia and the increased world and American demand for proteins, fats, and oils during the war and postwar periods. Other related factors that contributed to the expansion of the crop were (1) the relaxation of acreage controls; (2) the use of price supports; (3) the increased livestock population and the resultant requirements for soybean meal; (4) the increasing use of soybean oil in margarine, and shortening; and (5) the technological progress in the producing, processing, and utilization of the soybean.

In order to provide a basis for the examination of the competitive position of the Minnesota soybean producer within this international and national framework, the following hypothesis was set forth: *Minnesota has a comparative advantage in the production of soybeans, and in consequence soybeans can compete effectively with other farm enterprises.*

In general, the analysis presented in this study has tended to confirm this hypothesis. The facts which support this conclusion and which have been effective in accounting for the twofold increase in soybean production in Minnesota during the last five years are as follows:

(1) The net income per acre of soybeans is relatively higher than that of any other crop with the exception of corn.

(2) The development of new varieties of soybeans that are more adaptable to the present growing area in southern Minnesota and new varieties that can be used in other areas of the state will enhance the comparative advantage of the crop in the state. These varieties, such as the Blackhawk, induce greater yields and increase the oil content of the soybeans produced in the state.

(3) The producer in Minnesota has excellent present markets for his soybean production by virtue of the expanding market of the Minnesota and northern Iowa processing industry, and the potential export market in Canada.

(4) The study of fifty farms in southern Minnesota substantiates the rapid growth of soybean production in the state and indicates both an increase in the number of farms producing soybeans and an expansion in soybean acreage by established soybean farmers.

However, there are certain political and economic conditions that may limit the expansion of the soybean crop in Minnesota.

If more peaceful conditions return in Asia, that part of the world will be able to return to its prewar levels of soybean production and be able to regain its lost soybean export markets in Europe and elsewhere. The most important condition favorable to the Asiatic producer is the fact that the world's greatest potential demand for fats and oils exists in the deficit-soybean-producing countries of Europe that are short of American dollars and would, therefore, be more inclined to trade with Asia than the United States. Another unfavorable condition that affects the American soybean producer is that of the weakened soybean oil market. The rapid increase in the supply of cottonseed oil and the excellent world crop of olive oil have depressed the edible-oil market. Offsetting factors to the weakened export and oil market are the continued use of E.C.A. funds for the purchase of soybeans and soybean oil in this country, and more important, the phenomenal demand for soybean meal caused by an increased livestock population. If the protein needs of our present livestock population were adequately met, a

500-million-bushel crop of soybeans would be necessary, or a "crushing" crop of almost twice the size of our present one. The general outlook for the future production of the crop in the United States leads one to the conclusion that the rate of expansion of the crop will be more moderate.

The policies of the government also affect the possible trend of soybean production in Minnesota. Decisions as to cotton-acreage controls in the south may encourage more rapid expansion of the soybean crop in this area rather than in the northern Corn Belt states. In addition, changing the relationship between price supports for corn and for soybeans may give further impetus to the increased production of the crop that has the strongest market position at the time these price supports are announced.

Another situation which has a bearing on the possible trend of soybean production in Minnesota is that revealed in the study of fifty southern Minnesota farms from 1941 through 1950. This study indicates that the soybean crop is not yet a permanent part of the Minnesota farmer's crop rotation plan. More farms are producing soybeans in Minnesota, and former producers are expanding the proportion of their farm devoted to the crop. However, no consistent pattern has developed. In the past, hay and pasture acreage decreased to permit the expansion of the soybean acreage. In more recent years, no particular crop has been the main competitor of the soybean. The late planting of the crop leads to many last-minute production decisions. The wet springs in Minnesota that have kept farmers out of the fields have led to the expansion of the crop, but the weather is an influence that cannot be appraised accurately from year to year.

In conclusion, the factors supporting the continued expansion of the soybean crop in Minnesota are much stronger than the limiting conditions. Taking all factors together, one may conclude that soybean production will continue to increase in Minnesota, but at a declining rate.

THE PROCESSOR

The processing industry in the United States responded quickly to the demand for processed meal and oil. Today, the industry has overexpanded its processing capacity in relation to the available soybean crop. This has meant intense competition. This intensive competition has resulted in the following characteristics of the industry:

(1) the development of efficient large-scale hexane solvent extraction plants requiring high original investment costs
(2) the growth of vertically integrated companies, especially those concerns in the mixed-feed industry that want to be certain of soybean meal supplies
(3) the limitation of the number of firms that are financially able to meet such large-scale competition, which in turn has resulted in concentration of ownership in the industry
(4) the growth of small, privately and cooperatively owned, local processing plants. This last indicates the influence of location advantages that decrease the importance of the cost differentials between large-scale and small operations.

The above characteristics are also evident in the development of the processing industry in Minnesota, in the following ways:

(1) The principal processing method employed in the state, volumewise, is that of the hexane-solvent extraction-process.

(2) Vertical integration is illustrated in the state by the fact that three of the state's processing firms also produce their own mixed feeds.

(3) The characteristic of the importance of a few major firms in the industry appears in the fact that two processing plants operate approximately two thirds of the state's crushing capacity.

(4) The existence of small, local processing plants that take advantage of a local supply of soybeans and a local meal market is demonstrated by the recent construction in Minnesota of privately and cooperatively owned trichlorethylene-solvent extraction-plants. However, the meal produced by the trichlorethylene process has been found to be toxic to cattle. Therefore, two of these plants have ceased operation.

In order to provide a basis for the examination of the competitive position of the Minnesota soybean processor within this general framework of the processing industry the following hypothesis was set forth: *The processing industry in Minnesota possesses a highly favorable comparative advantage in relation to the processing industries located in the other principal processing states, and in consequence can compete effectively with the latter.*

The subsequent analysis confirms this hypothesis. The factors which support this conclusion are the location advantages of the Minnesota processor. These advantages are twofold:

(1) The Minnesota processor is able to sell his meal within the state or to western states and Canada where he does not compete with the Decatur location, and he charges a Decatur price plus the freight cost from Decatur to the point of sale. The difference between the freight charge from Decatur to the point of sale and the freight charge from the processing plant to the point of sale becomes an additional profit to the Minnesota processor.

(2) The other main saving is derived from the fact that the Minnesota processor bases his purchase price of soybeans on the Chicago market less freight from the point of production.

The advantages of the Decatur-plus-freight sale of meal and the Chicago-minus-freight purchase of soybeans by the Minnesota processor are maximized when the supply of soybeans and the market for meal are in the immediate locality of the processing plant. These necessary conditions for the maximization of the transportation advantages are present in Minnesota. They are as follows:

(1) Plentiful local supplies of soybeans exist for the processor, and the state is thought of as a "surplus" soybean-producing state in the sense that more soybeans are produced than are crushed by the processing industry.

(2) The local meal market is also excellent. The state has yet to produce all the soybean meal consumed by the Minnesota livestock population. The state is thought of as a deficit soybean-meal-producing state in the sense that more meal is consumed within the state than is produced.

(3) The storage facilities of the processors are also adequate to permit them to take advantage of the purchase of local soybean supplies at the time of crop movement.

However, there are certain disadvantageous conditions that apply to the Minnesota location and other limiting factors that affect the processing industry as a whole. The adverse conditions of the Minnesota location include the following: (1) the low oil content of Minnesota soybeans; (2) the transportation cost of shipping soybean oil to eastern markets on a Decatur freight basis; (3) the restricted area to which the meal transportation advantage applies; and (4) the temporary disadvantage of the Minnesota location if ceiling prices on soybeans become operative and are not based on the normal price differentials of soybeans between Minnesota and the other principal soybean producing states.

The over-all profit situation in the processing industry today (March 1952) is very poor. The holding tendency of the farmer has maintained the price of soybeans at a fairly high level, soybean meal prices are at ceiling, and soybean oil is less than half the ceiling price. In consequence, the crushing margin of the processor (the difference between the price of soybeans and the price of meal and oil) is not adequate to cover processing costs. This situation has led to custom processing for mixed-feed manufacturers, "mineralized" versions of soybean meal, and barter arrangements with farmers, whereby meal is exchanged for soybeans. It has led also to the construction of even larger processing plants in order to reduce per-unit costs of production. This additional construction has enlarged still further the excess crushing capacity of the soybean industry, competition thus being increased even more.

The location advantages of the Minnesota processor more than offset the disadvantages. Even in this relatively adverse period of the industry, the Minnesota crushing margin, on the whole, has been adequate to cover the state's weighted processing cost of 26.5 cents a bushel, and the differences in transportation advantages within the state are large enough to permit a range of processing costs from 20 cents to 54 cents a bushel.

In conclusion, the rapid growth of the processing industry in the United States has created an over-capacity situation. The maturing of this industry is now taking place, and some contraction is feasible. Expansion in favorable locations such as Minnesota, however, will probably continue, but at a pace slower than that of the last few years.

The firms that will expand processing operations in Minnesota are limited by the high original-investment cost necessary in this industry and by the importance of the hexane-solvent extraction-method. The advantages of the solvent method in reducing labor costs and increasing oil yields have not proved practicable in small operations. Most hexane-solvent firms refuse to build processing plants that are below 100-ton capacity per day, as they realize the advantage of lower labor costs would not be present to offset the high building costs. Trichlorethylene-solvent processing plants have been built with as small a capacity as 25 tons per day. But the per-bushel costs of processing by these firms are the highest in the industry, and operations have not proved advantageous even when the transportation savings were maximized by a local supply of soybeans and a local meal market. Furthermore, the toxic effect to cattle of the meal produced by this process is an even more important reason why this type of operation will probably not be undertaken in the future expansion of processing within the state. In all probability the present trichlorethylene plants in the state will cease operations.

The further expansion of the soybean-processing industry in the state will probably occur in the following manner: (1) through the expansion of present processing facilities, and (2) through the construction of new processing plants by well-established and well-integrated firms.

The adverse crushing margin present in the soybean processing industry (March 1952), if continued, will encourage present processors in Minnesota to expand their operations in order to lower unit-costs of production. The most economical way to achieve this expansion is to make use of present facilities and thus decrease the amount of additional investment needed.

The construction of new processing plants in the state will probably be undertaken by well-established and well-integrated firms that can afford the high original-investment cost and are flexible enough in their operations to take advantage of changing, local market conditions and the changing relationships between the two oilseed crops present in Minnesota.

Appendix I. Tables

TABLE 1. Soybeans: Acreage, Yield per Acre, and Production in Specified Countries, Average 1935–1939, Annual 1948–1950[1]

Continent and Country	Acreage, Thousand Acres[2]				Yield per Acre, Bushels				Production, Thousand Bushels			
	Average 1935–1939	1948	1949	1950[3]	Average 1935–1939	1948	1949	1950[3]	Average 1935–1939	1948	1949	1950[3]
North America												
Canada	10[4]	94	104	142	20.7	19.4	25.1	21.4	207[4]	1,824	2,605	3,039
United States[5]	3,042	10,430	10,156	13,291	18.5	21.4	22.7	21.6	56,167	223,006	230,997	287,010
Europe												
Bulgaria	34	.....	.....	.....	12.1	...	...	...	416	......	......	......
Hungary	7[6]	6	.....	.....	16.9	15.1	...	...	125[6]	90	......	......
Italy	..[7]	5	3	2	12.1	21.9	18.3	24.7	1	107	52	46
Roumania	49[4]	..	..	..	9.5	...	...	...	463[4]	...	..	..
U.S.S.R. (Europe and Asia)	607[6]	..	..	..	...	...	...	...	5,805[6]	...	..	.
Asia												
Turkey	1[6]	5	5	5	29.0	15.3	10.6	14.9	37[6]	71	50	73
China (22 provinces)	12,411	11,309	11,762	...	16.7	18.6	15.2	...	207,666	210,820	179,200	......
Manchuria	8,992	.....	5,500	...	16.8	...	12.0	...	151,214	......	66,000	......
Japan	812[4]	584	648	734	15.4	13.8	13.8	17.1	12,499	8,085	8,928	12,566
Taiwan (Formosa)	17[4]	50	...	.....	8.9	9.1	...	...	151[4]	457	.....	......
Korea[8]	1,921[4]	487	658	.....	10.0	10.1	10.0	...	17,654	4,924	6,654	......
Indonesia[9]	889	900	872	.....	10.9	10.9	11.2	...	9,731	9,847	9,737	......

TABLE 1. *Continued*

Continent and Country	Acreage, Thousand Acres [2]				Yield per Acre, Bushels				Production, Thousand Bushels			
	Average 1935–1939	1948	1949	1950 [3]	Average 1935–1939	1948	1949	1950 [3]	Average 1935–1939	1948	1949	1950 [3]
Africa												
Tanganyika	.....	...	...	.....	...	...	...	...	......	97	36	67
Union of South Africa	.....	13 [10]	15 [10]	.....	...	5.0	5.3	...	......	67	80	......
World total [11]	29,100	31,700	31,300	36,130	...	...	...	...	463,900	563,200	510,170	626,000

[1] Years shown refer to years of harvest. Southern Hemisphere crops which are harvested in the early part of the year are combined with those of the Northern Hemisphere harvested in the latter part of the same year.

[2] Figures refer to harvested areas as far as possible.

[3] Preliminary.

[4] Average of less than 5 years.

[5] Acreage harvested for beans.

[6] One year only.

[7] Less than 500 acres.

[8] Beginning with 1948, figures represent South Korea only.

[9] Java and Madura only before 1948.

[10] Planted acreage.

[11] Includes estimates for the above countries for which data are not available and for minor producing countries.

Data published by Office of Foreign Agricultural Relations, U.S. Department of Agriculture. Prepared or estimated on the basis of official statistics of foreign governments, reports of the U.S. Foreign Service officers, result of office research, or other information. Prewar estimates for countries having changed boundaries have been adjusted to conform to present boundaries, except as noted.

Source: *Soybean Blue Book*, 1951.

TABLE 2. Soybeans: Exports from Specified Countries, Average 1935–1939, Annual 1947–1950

Country	Number of Thousand Bushels				
	Average 1935–1939	1947	1948	1949	1950 [1]
United States	4,793 [2]	2,505	6,497	23,361	19,110
China	137	2,200	925	.....	.....
Manchuria	69,186	....	....	.....	.....
Japan	43	....	....	.....	.....
Korea	3,300	....	....	.....	.....
Turkey	.....	18	36	4	18
Bulgaria	295	....	....	.....	.....
Indonesia	225	....	250	11	.....

[1] Preliminary.
[2] Average of less than 5 years.

TABLE 3. Soybean Oil: Exports from Specified Countries, Average 1935–1939, Annual 1947–1950

Country	Number of Short Tons				
	Average 1935–1939	1947	1948	1949	1950 [1]
United States	3,234	51,587	41,517	188,244	152,105
China	318	1,330	61	......	......
Manchuria	77,924	.....	.....	......	......
United Kingdom	10,585	20	.....	......	......
Netherlands	9,244	243	270	6,916	2,024
Denmark	13,752	12	35	86	54
Sweden	4,805	0	0	......	......
Japan	5,087	.....	.....	......	......

[1] Preliminary.

TABLE 4. Suez Canal: Northbound Movement of Manchurian Soybeans, December 1950–June 1951

National Origin of Vessel	Date of Arrival	Tons [1]	From	To
Italy	Dec. 7	9,448	Dairen	Rotterdam
Greece	Dec. 9	9,900	Dairen	Genoa
Greece	Dec. 10	9,656	Dairen	Genoa
Greece	Dec. 13	10,436	Dairen	Rotterdam
Honduras	Dec. 19	8,500	Dairen	Marseilles
Panama	Dec. 23	10,300	Dairen	United Kingdom f.o.[2]
Britain	Jan. 2	8,770	Dairen	United Kingdom f.o.[2]
Greece	Jan. 6	9,097	Dairen	United Kingdom f.o.[2]
Morocco	Jan. 10	6,500	Dairen	Copenhagen
Greece	Jan. 12	10,200	Dairen	Copenhagen
Greece	Jan. 16	9,370	Dairen	Hamburg
Canada	Jan. 21	9,650	Dairen	Antwerp
U.S.S.R.	Jan. 22	7,000	Vladivostock	Gdynia, Poland
Greece	Jan. 29	10,000	Dairen	Hamburg
Britain	Feb. 4	10,000	Dairen	Aarhus
Britain	Feb. 6	9,496	Dairen	Rotterdam
U.S.S.R.	Feb. 7	4,800	Vladivostock	Antwerp
U.S.S.R.	Feb. 26	6,008	Dairen	Antwerp
Panama	Mar. 17	6,600	Dairen	Stettin
Greece	Mar. 26	9,900	Dairen	Antwerp
Liberia	Apr. 10	10,450	Dairen	Rotterdam
Britain	Apr. 11	7,735	Chefoo	Hamburg
Panama	Apr. 11	10,485	Dairen	Antwerp
Liberia	Apr. 20	10,350	Dairen	Rotterdam
Britain	Apr. 21	9,216	Dairen	Gdynia, Poland
Panama	Apr. 28	8,700	Dairen	Hamburg
	May 3	10,000	Dairen	Denmark
	May 5	10,000	Dairen	Gdynia, Poland
	June 9	9,793		
	June	6,800		
	June	2,800		
Total		271,960		

[1] Presumed to be metric tons.
[2] f.o. = for order. American Consulate, Port Said, Egypt.

TABLE 5. Soybeans: Acreage, Yield, and Production in the United States, 1924–1950

Year	Number of Thousand Acres						Average Yield per Acre Harvested		Total Production	
	Planted			Harvested						
	Grown Alone	Inter-planted [1]	Equivalent Solid [2]	for Beans	for Hay	Grazed or Plowed Under	for Beans, Bushels	for Hay, Tons	Beans, Thousand Bushels	Hay, Thousand Tons
1924	1,567	417	1,782	448	1,147	187	11.0	1.13	4,947	1,299
1925	1,539	476	1,785	415	1,175	195	11.7	1.01	4,875	1,185
1926	1,871	502	2,127	466	1,431	230	11.2	1.18	5,239	1,687
1927	2,057	571	2,350	568	1,556	226	12.2	1.18	6,938	1,837
1928	2,154	556	2,439	579	1,609	251	13.6	1.23	7,880	1,974
1929	2,429	743	2,807	708	1,774	325	13.3	1.16	9,438	2,051
1930	3,072	786	3,473	1,074	2,062	337	13.0	.94	13,929	1,938
1931	3,835	909	4,304	1,141	2,772	391	15.1	1.26	17,260	3,479
1932	3,704	893	4,165	1,001	2,738	486	15.1	1.25	15,158	3,433
1933	3,537	813	3,957	1,044	2,506	407	12.9	1.16	13,509	2,917
1934	5,764	858	6,207	1,556	4,227	424	14.9	1.08	23,157	4,545
1935	6,966	1,028	7,503	2,915	4,044	544	16.8	1.34	48,901	5,422
1936	6,127	2,115	7,183	2,359	3,116	1,708	14.3	.96	33,721	3,002
1937	6,332	2,261	7,464	2,586	3,459	1,409	17.9	1.36	46,164	4,731
1938	7,312	2,541	8,587	3,035	3,724	1,828	20.4	1.43	61,906	5,335
1939	9,565	2,710	10,920	4,315	4,590	2,015	20.9	1.48	90,141	6,772
1940	10,487	2,589	11,782	4,807	4,819	2,156	16.2	1.34	78,045	6,450
1941	10,068	2,555	11,345	5,889	3,546	1,910	18.2	1.30	107,197	4,616
1942	13,696	2,426	14,912	9,894	2,621	2,397	19.0	1.36	187,584	3,535
1943	14,191	2,475	15,428	10,397	3,177	1,854	18.3	1.21	190,133	3,837
1944	13,118	1,861	14,050	10,232	2,583	1,235	18.8	1.18	191,958	3,041
1945	13,007	1,537	13,777	10,661	1,939	1,177	18.0	1.28	192,076	2,476
1946	11,662	1,530	12,427	9,806	1,533	1,088	20.5	1.29	261,275	1,984
1947	12,956	1,506	13,709	11,212	1,333	1,164	16.4	1.22	183,558	1,631
1948	11,843	1,390	12,538	10,430	1,160	948	21.4	1.34	223,006	1,550
1949	11,628	1,346	12,301	10,156	1,168	977	22.7	1.40	230,897	1,633
1950	14,704	1,408	15,408	13,291	1,151	966	21.6	1.33	287,010	1,533

[1] Grown with other crops.
[2] Acreage grown alone, with an allowance for acreage grown with other crops.

TABLE 6. Acreage of Soybeans Harvested for Beans, United States and Selected Groups of States, Averages 1925–1929, 1930–1934, and 1935–1939, and Annually 1940–1950

Period or Year	Number of Thousand Acres						
	United States	Corn Belt [1]	Lake States [2]	Plains States [3]	Delta States [4]	Atlantic States [5]	All Other States
1925–1929	547	337	4	4	38	118	46
1930–1934	1,163	877	9	10	45	160	62
1935–1939	3,042	2,604	44	7	97	209	81
1940	4,807	4,097	155	31	117	283	124
1941	5,889	4,938	217	69	203	317	145
1942	9,894	7,898	484	269	480	470	293
1943	10,397	8,482	410	345	428	425	307
1944	10,232	8,697	412	217	332	333	241
1945	10,661	8,933	611	270	294	359	194
1946	9,806	7,863	729	246	392	344	232
1947	11,212	8,806	1,022	310	402	414	258
1948	10,430	8,080	924	331	432	444	220
1949	10,158	7,784	790	303	424	459	326
1950	13,291	9,707	1,198	512	878	521	475

[1] Illinois, Iowa, Indiana, Ohio, and Missouri.
[2] Minnesota, Wisconsin, and Michigan.
[3] Kansas, Nebraska, South Dakota, and North Dakota.
[4] Arkansas, Mississippi, and Louisiana.
[5] North Carolina, Virginia, Maryland, and Delaware.

TABLE 7. Soybeans: Supply and Utilization in the United States, 1924–1950, by Number of Thousand Bushels

Year Beginning October 1	Supply				Utilization					
	Total Stocks Oct. 1 [1]	Production [2]	Imports for Consumption	Total Supply [3]	Seed	Feed [4]	Processed for Oil and Meal	Exporting [5]	Other Uses [6]	Carry-Over, Sept. 30 [7]
1924	5	4,947	60	5,012	1,900	1,207	307	.....	1,596	2
1925	2	4,275	71	4,948	2,289	1,174	351	.....	1,134	... [8]
1926	... [8]	5,239	67	5,306	2,525	1,311	335	.....	1,133	2
1927	2	6,938	70	7,010	2,687	1,631	559	.....	2,133	... [8]
1928	... [8]	7,880	77	7,957	2,984	1,473	882	.....	2,548	70
1929	70	9,438	64	9,572	3,762	1,730	1,666	.....	2,298	116
1930	116	13,929	54	14,099	4,724	2,763	4,069	.....	2,049	494
1931	494	17,260	49	17,803	4,633	2,867	4,725	2,161	3,295	122
1932	122	15,158	13	15,293	4,490	2,264	3,470	2,450	2,561	58
1933	58	13,509	6	13,573	7,615	2,111	3,054	.....	767	26
1934	26	23,157	5	23,188	10,066	2,036	9,105	19	1,643	319
1935	319	48,901	4	49,224	8,875	3,898	25,181	3,490	7,419	361
1936	361	33,721	17	34,099	9,539	2,741	20,618	19	889	293
1937	293	46,164	3	46,460	10,947	3,273	30,310	1,392	198	340
1938	340	61,906	3	62,249	14,667	4,554	44,642	4,424	−7,009	965
1939	965	90,141	2	91,108	15,974	5,365	56,684	10,979	1,713	393
1940	393	78,045	1	78,439	15,141	4,999	64,056	284	−6,731	690
1941	690	107,197	.. [8]	107,887	20,385	3,925	77,151	489	−72	6,009
1942	6,009	187,524	.. [8]	193,533	20,980	6,016	133,454	917	19,629	12,537
1943	12,537	190,133	.. [8]	202,670	19,758	5,496	142,306	962	19,995	14,153
1944	14,153	191,958	4	206,111	18,885	3,598	153,402	5,090	17,398	7,738

TABLE 7. *Continued*

Year Beginning October 1	Supply				Utilization					
	Total Stocks Oct. 1[1]	Production[2]	Imports for Consumption	Total Supply[3]	Seed	Feed[4]	Processed for Oil and Meal	Exporting[5]	Other Uses[6]	Carry-Over, Sept. 30[7]
1945	7,738	192,076	..[8]	199,814	16,473	3,724	159,460	2,858	12,973	4,326
1946	4,326	201,275	..[8]	205,601	17,137	2,516	170,245	3,880	6,462	5,361
1947	5,361	183,558	..[8]	188,919	15,665	2,315	161,397	2,943	4,035	2,564
1948	2,564	223,006	7	225,577	15,381	2,609	183,664	23,010	−2,194	3,107
1949	3,107	230,897	4	234,008	19,000	2,933	195,115	13,137	955	2,868
1950	2,868	287,010								

[1] Factory and warehouse stocks only, through October 1, 1941; total stocks, October 1, 1942, and subsequently.

[2] Crop of year listed first; e.g., the 1924 crop was 4,947,000 bushels.

[3] Sum of stocks, production, and imports. The "total supply" figures for years previous to 1942–1943 are incomplete to the extent that they do not include stocks on farms, in country elevators, and at terminal markets. (Such stocks were not reported previous to October 1, 1942.) Figures are not adjusted for new crop soybeans used in September. Use in September of year of harvest is estimated for recent years as follows: 0.6 million bushels in 1947, 4.9 million bushels in 1948, 8.8 million bushels in 1949, and 2.7 million bushels in 1950.

[4] Fed to livestock on farms where produced.

[5] Data not available for years previous to 1931–1932. Includes shipments to U.S. Territories in 1937–1938 and subsequent years.

[6] Residual item. This includes soybeans fed to livestock other than on farms where the soybeans were produced. It may also include small quantities used for human food. Prior to 1931–1932 it includes exports. Prior to 1937–1938 it includes shipments to U.S. territories. The minus quantities shown for three years prior to 1942–1943 are explainable by the fact that there were unreported supplies (stocks, October 1) on farms, in country elevators, and in terminal markets.

[7] Factory and warehouse stocks only, through September 30, 1941; total stocks, September 30, 1942, and subsequently.

[8] Less than 500 bushels.

TABLE 8. Acreage Changes in the Six Leading Soybean States

Year	Number of Thousand Acres						
	Corn	Flax	Soy-beans	Bar-ley	Oats	Wheat	Hay and Pasture
			Illinois				
1939–1948 average[1]	8,332	...	3,044	79	3,428	1,427	2,839
1944[2]	9,140	...	3,430	42	3,011	1,210	2,150
1949	9,112	...	3,135	38	3,654	1,859	2,591
1950[1]	8,234	...	3,948	48	3,911	1,376	2,797
			Iowa				
1939–1948 average	10,226	157	1,471	156	5,277	215	3,521
1944	10,631	91	1,906	6	4,644	112	2,611
1949[2]	10,848	110	1,312	30	6,087	382	3,143
1950	9,865	82	1,921	60	6,457	262	3,648
			Minnesota				
1939–1948 average	5,087	1,320	377	1,261	4,548	1,275	4,351
1944	4,502	817	243	624	4,625	....	1,316
1949	4,826	1,639	753	1,048	4,860	1,133	1,560
1950	5,111	1,205	1,057	1,252	5,101	921	3,812
			Missouri				
1939–1948 average	4,242	...	507	122	1,815	1,342	3,603
1944	4,586	...	680	77	1,282	1,175	2,915
1949	3,743	...	884	76	1,335	1,617	5,103
1950	4,158	...	1,191	80	1,782	1,362	3,696
			Indiana				
1939–1948 average	4,292	...	1,228	48	1,278	1,403	1,896
1944	4,410	...	1,470	44	1,096	1,257	1,817
1949	4,469	...	1,407	20	1,330	1,696	2,050
1950	4,319	...	1,591	25	1,421	1,479	1,850
			Ohio				
1939–1948 average	3,436	...	906	30	1,101	1,932	2,556
1944	3,424	...	1,223	20	1,017	1,891	1,867
1949	3,246	...	828	15	1,211	2,238	2,049
1950	3,364	...	1,056	26	1,147	2,118	2,680

[1] The data for the 1939–1948 averages and for 1950 were all derived from *Crops and Markets,* U.S. Department of Agriculture, Vol. 28 (1951 edition), which included hay instead of pasture acreage.

[2] The data for 1944 in Illinois and for 1944 and 1949 in the other states were derived from the 1950 Census of Agriculture, preliminary, including crop land used only for pasture.

TABLE 9. Soybeans Harvested for Beans: Acreage, Yield, and Production for the Ten Leading States, 1945–1950

Year	Acreage, Thousand Acres	Yield per Acre, Bushels	Production, Thousand Bushels	Year	Acreage, Thousand Acres	Yield per Acre, Bushels	Production, Thousand Bushels
	Arkansas				Illinois		
1945	209	16.0	3,344	1945	3,760	20.0	75,200
1946	295	18.5	5,458	1946	3,320	23.5	78,020
1947	283	12.0	3,396	1947	3,636	18.0	65,448
1948	264	19.5	5,148	1948	3,354	24.0	80,496
1949	291	20.0	5,820	1949	3,287	26.0	85,462
1950	556	21.0	11,676	1950	3,948	24.0	94,752
	Indiana				Iowa		
1945	1,466	19.5	22,587	1945	1,910	18.5	35,335
1946	1,374	19.0	26,106	1946	1,548	23.0	35,604
1947	1,503	18.5	27,806	1947	1,884	15.5	29,202
1948	1,459	22.0	32,098	1948	1,564	22.5	35,190
1949	1,442	24.0	34,608	1949	1,340	23.0	30,820
1950	1,591	22.0	35,002	1950	1,921	22.0	42,262
	Kansas				Minnesota		
1945	235	10.0	2,350	1945	452	14.5	6,554
1946	198	11.0	2,178	1946	610	17.5	10,675
1947	222	8.5	1,887	1947	920	15.0	13,800
1948	167	15.0	2,505	1948	844	18.5	15,614
1949	237	14.5	3,436	1949	709	18.0	12,762
1950	359	18.0	6,462	1950	1,057	15.5	16,384
	Mississippi				Missouri		
1945	62	13.0	806	1945	720	13.0	9,360
1946	70	15.0	1,050	1946	718	20.0	14,360
1947	95	14.0	1,330	1947	825	12.0	9,900
1948	133	18.0	2,394	1948	795	20.0	15,900
1949	108	16.5	1,782	1949	857	21.0	17,997
1950	282	24.0	6,768	1950	1,191	23.0	27,393
	North Carolina				Ohio		
1945	216	12.5	2,700	1945	1,077	18.0	19,386
1946	212	13.5	2,862	1946	903	18.0	16,254
1947	233	15.0	3,495	1947	950	18.5	17,575
1948	264	13.5	3,564	1948	908	20.5	18,614
1949	264	16.0	4,224	1949	858	24.0	20,592
1950	301	17.0	5,117	1950	1,056	22.0	23,232

TABLE 10. Soybeans: Yield per Acre, Oil Content, and Oil Yield per Acre in the Principal Soybean-Producing States, by States, 1944 and 1945[1]

State	1944			1945			1944–1945 Average		
	Yield per Acre, Bushels[2]	Oil Content, Percentage[3]	Oil Yield per Acre, Pounds	Yield per Acre, Bushels[2]	Oil Content, Percentage	Oil Yield per Acre, Pounds	Yield per Acre, Bushels	Oil Content, Percentage	Oil Yield per Acre, Pounds
Alabama	10.0	20.2	121.2	11.0	20.5	135.3	10.5	20.3	127.9
Arkansas	15.3	20.7	192.5	16.0	21.3	204.5	15.8	21.0	199.1
Georgia	6.0	20.0	72.0	7.5	19.9	89.6	6.8	20.0	81.6
Illinois	21.4	20.8	267.1	20.0	20.2	242.4	20.7	20.5	254.6
Indiana	17.2	20.2	208.5	19.5	20.0	234.0	18.4	20.1	221.9
Iowa	20.3	20.2	246.0	18.5	20.0	222.0	19.4	20.1	234.0
Kansas	13.7	20.2	166.0	10.0	21.2	127.2	11.9	20.7	147.8
Kentucky	15.0	20.2	181.8	16.0	19.9	191.0	15.5	20.0	186.0
Louisiana	12.0	20.7	149.0	14.0	19.9	167.2	13.0	20.2	157.6
Michigan	17.0	19.3	196.9	17.5	19.4	203.7	17.3	19.3	199.3
Minnesota	15.4	18.6	171.9	14.5	19.6	170.5	15.0	19.1	171.9
Mississippi	12.0	20.7	149.0	13.0	21.2	165.4	12.5	20.9	156.8
Missouri	17.5	20.8	218.4	13.0	20.9	163.0	15.3	20.9	191.9
Nebraska	17.8	19.6	209.3	18.0	20.3	219.2	17.9	20.0	214.8
North Carolina	10.5	19.3	121.6	12.5	19.5	146.2	11.5	19.4	133.9
North Dakota	10.5	19.3	121.6	11.5	19.4	133.9	11.0	19.3	127.4
Ohio	17.6	20.2	213.3	18.0	20.0	216.0	17.8	20.1	214.7
South Carolina	7.0	20.3	85.3	7.0	20.0	84.0	7.0	20.2	84.8
South Dakota	17.0	19.2	195.8	14.0	19.5	163.8	15.5	19.3	179.5
Tennessee	15.0	20.7	186.3	14.5	20.3	176.6	14.8	20.5	122.0
Virginia	15.0	19.4	176.6	16.0	19.8	190.1	15.5	19.5	181.4
Wisconsin	12.8	18.6	142.8	15.0	20.1	180.9	13.9	19.3	161.0

[1] Noriar Pahigian, *Marketing Study of the Oil Content of Soybeans as Related to Production Acres and Climate* (P.M.A., U.S. Department of Agriculture, Washington, D.C., September 1950).
[2] From *Soybeans Harvested for Beans*, an annual report by the B.A.E., U.S. Department of Agriculture.
[3] Computed from CCC records and converted to moisture-free basis.

TABLE 11. Soybean Oil Content, Temperature, and Length of Day in the Principal Soybean-Producing States, May–October Averages, 1944 and 1945[1]

State	1944		1945		
	Oil Content, Percentage	Temperature, Degrees F.	Oil Content, Percentage	Temperature, Degrees F.	Length of Day, Hours
Alabama	17.5	76.3	17.6	76.4	13.1
Arkansas	17.8	73.2	18.3	72.2	13.4
Georgia	17.1	77.3	17.1	76.6	13.6
Illinois	17.9	73.9	17.4	70.9	14.0
Indiana	17.4	73.5	17.2	70.8	14.0
Iowa	17.4	70.0	17.2	67.9	14.1
Kansas	17.5	75.0	18.2	73.2	13.8
Kentucky	17.4	71.5	17.1	70.3	13.3
Louisiana	17.8	80.0	17.1	78.7	13.5
Michigan	16.6	66.4	16.7	63.5	14.2
Minnesota	16.0	61.7	16.9	59.5	13.7
Mississippi	17.8	78.7	18.2	77.3	13.6
Missouri	17.9	74.8	18.0	72.7	13.9
Nebraska	16.9	70.1	17.5	68.4	14.0
North Carolina	16.6	71.5	16.8	70.7	13.4
North Dakota	16.6	62.9	16.7	61.7	14.5
Ohio	17.5	71.5	17.2	69.7	14.0
South Carolina	17.5	74.6	17.2	74.0	13.3
South Dakota	16.5	66.5	16.8	75.4	14.4
Tennessee	17.8	72.9	17.5	71.8	13.2
Virginia	16.7	69.7	17.0	69.6	13.3
Wisconsin	16.0	66.9	17.3	63.9	14.3

[1] Noriar Pahigian, *Marketing Study of the Oil Content of Soybeans as Related to Production Areas and Climate* (P.M.A., U.S. Department of Agriculture, Washington, D.C., September 1950). Computed from records of the U.S. Naval Observatory.

State figures for average temperature and length of day are not adequate in several cases because the production of soybeans is concentrated in particular areas within these states.

Table 12. Soybean Oil Meal and Cake: Supply and Utilization in the United States, 1924 through 1949, by Number of Thousand Tons [1]

Year Beginning October 1	Supply			Utilization		
	Domestic Production	Imports	Total Supply	Exports	Food, Industry, and Other Non-Feed	Feed
1924	7.6	18.3	25.9	...	...	25.9
1925	8.6	19.8	28.4	...	...	28.4
1926	8.3	23.9	32.2	...	...	32.2
1927	13.7	47.7	61.4	...	...	61.4
1928	21.5	69.5	91.0	...	...	91.0
1929	40.7	73.5	114.2	...	...	114.2
1930	98.6	24.0	122.6	...	...	122.6
1931	114.7	18.6	133.3	...	...	133.3
1932	84.3	28.3	112.6	...	...	112.6
1933	73.9	25.0	98.9	...	...	98.9
1934	220.4	64.2	284.6	...	18.0	266.6
1935	613.1	20.0	633.1	...	19.0	614.1
1936	495.8	55.7	551.5	...	20.0	531.5
1937	724.1	15.5	739.6	...	21.0	718.6
1938	1,064.4	12.3	1,076.7	35.0	22.0	1,019.7
1939	1,348.8	12.1	1,360.9	62.3	23.0	1,275.6
1940	1,543.4	8.1	1,551.5	25.4	35.0	1,491.1
1941	1,844.9	0	1,844.9	19.7	40.1	1,785.1
1942	3,200.3	0	3,200.3	20.9	105.5	3,073.9
1943	3,446.0	0	3,446.0	16.1	107.1	3,322.6
1944	3,698.5	0	3,698.5	10.0	61.4	3.627.1
1945	3,837.3	..	3,837.3	.9	181.4	3,655.0
1946	4,086.4	0	4,086.4	141.7	199.3	3,745.4
1947	3,832.7	0	3,832.7	95.7	353.8	3,383.2
1948	4,330.4	3.2	4,333.6	150.1	27.8	4,155.7
1949	4,581.7	26.1	4,607.8	47.4	46.9	4,513.5

[1] Source: *Soybean Blue Book*, 1951, p. 47.

TABLE 13. State-to-State Movements of Soybean Meal in the Six Main Meal-Producing States, 1948, 1949, and 1950 [1]

	Number of Cars			Percentage of Total		
	1948	1949	1950	1948	1949	1950
Illinois to:						
Alabama	3	5	1	1.1	1.3	0.2
Arkansas	3	2	5	1.1	0.5	1.2
California	1	..	3	0.4	...	0.7
Colorado	4	2	4	1.4	0.5	1.0
Connecticut	1	..	..	0.4	...	...
Delaware	4	3	13	1.4	0.8	3.1
Florida	..	1	1	...	0.3	0.2
Georgia	..	2	7	...	0.5	1.7
Idaho	1	..	1	0.4	...	0.2
Illinois	51	72	85	18.3	19.4	20.3
Indiana	19	34	21	6.8	9.2	5.0
Iowa	7	6	11	2.5	1.6	2.6
Kansas	3	3	3	1.1	0.8	0.7
Kentucky	7	10	2	2.5	2.7	0.5
Louisiana	6	7	6	2.2	1.9	1.4
Maine	..	1	..	...	0.3	...
Maryland	..	3	5	...	0.8	1.2
Massachusetts	1	4	3	0.4	1.1	0.7
Michigan	13	16	20	4.7	4.3	4.8
Minnesota	11	2	2	4.0	0.5	0.5
Mississippi	..	..	1	...	...	0.2
Missouri	9	9	26	3.2	2.4	6.2
Montana	1	..	..	0.4	...	...
Nebraska	1	2	3	0.4	0.5	0.7
New Jersey	2	5	1	0.7	1.3	0.2
New Mexico	..	..	2	...	...	0.5
New York	36	55	35	12.9	14.8	8.4
North Carolina	3	6	9	1.1	1.6	2.2
North Dakota	1	1	..	0.4	0.3	...
Ohio	29	40	46	10.4	10.8	11.0
Oklahoma	2	4	3	0.7	1.1	0.7
Pennsylvania	10	21	16	3.6	5.7	3.8
South Carolina	3	..	1	1.1	...	0.2
South Dakota	4	1	..	1.4	0.3	...
Tennessee	11	12	30	4.0	3.2	7.2
Texas	9	6	12	3.2	1.6	2.9
Utah	1	..	3	0.4	...	0.7
Vermont	5	12	5	1.8	3.2	1.2
Virginia	1	4	9	0.4	1.1	2.2
Washington	1	1	1	0.4	0.3	0.2
West Virginia	..	5	1	...	1.3	0.2
Wisconsin	12	14	19	4.3	3.8	4.5
Wyoming	2	..	2	0.7	...	0.5
Total in sample	278	371	418	100.2	99.8	99.7
Indiana to:						
Connecticut	..	..	1	...	...	1.3
Delaware	2	6	4	3.6	10.9	5.2
Illinois	..	..	..	...	...	...

TABLE 13. *Continued*

	Number of Cars			Percentage of Total		
	1948	1949	1950	1948	1949	1950
Indiana to:						
Indiana	10	6	8	18.2	10.9	10.4
Kentucky	..	..	3	...	...	3.9
Maryland	..	..	1	...	...	1.3
Massachusetts	..	..	1	...	...	1.3
Michigan	4	..	1	7.3	...	1.3
New Hampshire	1	..	..	1.8	...	...
New Jersey	1	3	2	1.8	5.5	2.6
New York	14	15	14	25.5	27.8	18.2
Ohio	17	18	26	30.9	32.7	33.8
Pennsylvania	5	5	5	9.1	9.1	6.5
South Carolina	1	..	..	1.8	...	...
Tennessee	..	..	1	...	...	1.3
Virginia	..	1	1	...	1.8	1.3
Vermont	..	1	8	...	1.8	10.4
West Virginia	..	..	1	...	...	1.3
Total in sample	55	55	77	100.0	100.5	100.1
Iowa to:						
Arizona	..	1	..	...	0.6	...
Arkansas	1	1	..	0.6	0.6	...
California	7	12	8	4.1	7.0	5.5
Colorado	7	4	6	4.1	2.3	4.1
Delaware	1	1	..	0.6	0.6	...
Idaho	1	1	3	0.6	0.6	2.1
Illinois	6	2	1	3.5	1.2	0.7
Indiana	1	..	..	0.6	...	...
Iowa	30	21	25	17.6	12.2	17.1
Kansas	6	6	8	3.5	3.5	5.5
Louisiana	2	3	..	1.2	1.7	...
Michigan	1	1	..	0.6	0.6	...
Minnesota	25	31	29	14.7	18.0	19.9
Missouri	17	18	13	10.0	10.5	8.9
Montana	1	3	2	0.6	1.7	1.4
Nebraska	11	30	19	6.5	17.4	13.0
New Mexico	1	..	..	0.6	...	...
New York	2	4	1	1.2	2.3	0.7
North Dakota	..	1	2	...	0.6	1.4
Ohio	5	3	1	2.9	1.7	0.7
Oklahoma	1	2	2	0.6	1.2	1.4
Oregon	4	3	1	2.4	1.7	0.7
Pennsylvania	1	..	..	0.6	...	...
South Dakota	1	1	2	0.6	0.6	1.4
Texas	11	6	6	6.5	3.5	4.1
Utah	4	7	4	2.4	4.1	2.7
Vermont	..	..	2	...	...	1.4
Washington	12	4	3	7.1	2.3	2.1
Wisconsin	10	5	7	5.9	2.9	4.8
Wyoming	1	1	1	0.6	0.6	0.7
Total in sample	170	172	146	100.2	100.0	100.3

Table 13. *Continued*

	Number of Cars			Percentage of Total		
	1948	1949	1950	1948	1949	1950
Ohio to:						
Connecticut	1	..	1	0.7	...	1.0
Delaware	4	11	8	2.9	9.8	7.6
Georgia	2	..	..	1.6	...	...
Florida	..	1	..	...	0.9	...
Illinois	..	1	..	...	0.9	...
Indiana	..	1	1	...	0.9	1.(
Kentucky	1	..	..	0.7	...	...
Louisiana	3	..	..	2.2	...	...
Maryland	6	5	5	4.4	4.5	4.8
Massachusetts	8	2	2	5.8	1.8	1.9
New Hampshire	..	1	..	...	0.9	...
New Jersey	4	4	5	2.9	3.6	4.8
New York	51	38	38	37.2	33.9	36.2
North Carolina	..	2	..	...	1.8	...
Ohio	25	18	9	18.2	16.1	8.6
Pennsylvania	17	21	26	12.4	18.8	24.8
Rhode Island	..	..	1	...	...	1.0
Vermont	7	5	2	5.1	4.5	1.9
Virginia	6	2	4	4.4	1.8	3.8
West Virginia	2	..	3	1.5	...	2.9
Total in sample	137	112	105	100.0	100.2	100.3
Missouri to:						
Arkansas	..	1	..	...	3.2	...
California	7	2	5	29.2	6.5	16.1
Colorado	1	2	..	4.2	6.5	...
Florida	..	2	..	...	6.5	...
Idaho	2	..	..	8.3	...	...
Illinois	..	..	1	...	...	3.2
Iowa	2	..	..	8.3	...	...
Kansas	2	3	2	8.3	9.7	6.5
Missouri	1	12	8	4.2	38.7	25.8
Montana	..	..	1	...	...	3.2
Nebraska	1	2	3	4.2	6.5	9.7
New York	1	..	..	4.2	...	...
Oklahoma	1	1	1	4.2	3.2	3.2
Oregon	..	..	1	...	...	3.2
Pennsylvania	2	..	..	8.3	...	...
South Dakota	..	..	..	...	...	...
Tennessee	..	..	4	...	...	12.9
Texas	1	4	5	4.2	12.9	16.1
Utah	1	1	..	4.2	3.2	...
Vermont	1	..	..	4.2	...	...
Wyoming	1	..	..	4.2	...	...
Washington	..	1	..	...	3.2	...
Total in sample	24	31	31	100.2	100.1	99.9

TABLE 13. *Continued*

	Number of Cars			Percentage of Total		
	1948	1949	1950	1948	1949	1950
Minnesota to:						
California	3	2	..	12.0	5.7	...
Idaho	2	1	1	8.0	2.9	2.9
Iowa	1	2	..	4.0	5.7	...
Louisiana	..	2	..	...	5.7	...
Minnesota	10	18	21	40.0	51.4	61.8
Nebraska	1	..	..	4.0	...	...
North Dakota	1	..	..	4.0	...	...
Oregon	1	1	2	4.0	2.9	5.9
Washington	..	6	7	...	17.1	20.6
Wisconsin	6	3	3	24.0	8.6	8.8
Total in sample	25	35	34	100.0	100.0	100.0

[1] Source: Interstate Commerce Commission, Carload Waybill Analyses, 1948, 1949, and 1950, *State-to-State Distribution of Products of Agriculture.*

TABLE 14. Protein Concentrates: Estimated Use for Feed in the United States, Prewar Average and Years 1944 through 1950, Year Beginning October 1, by Number of Thousand Tons[1]

Protein Concentrate	Average 1937–1941	1944	1945	1946	1947	1948	1949	1950[2]
Soybean cake and meal	1,258	3,627	3,655	3,745	3,383	4,156	4,514	5,200
Linseed cake and meal	481	459	563	370	606	620	670	625
Cottonseed cake and meal	1,958	1,982	1,433	1,434	1,953	2,271	2,375	1,700
Peanut cake and meal	74	96	90	98	122	96	93	75
Copra cake and meal	134	42	69	190	177	160	186	175
Gluten feed and meal	690	864	802	1,040	799	848	926	975
Tankage and meat scraps	728	792	745	740	823	854	841	850
Fish cake and meal	235	209	194	191	213	235	259	250
Dried milk products[3]	142	105	100	115	90	95	100	90
Other milk products[4]	1,829	1,465	1,360	1,300	1,260	1,280	1,300	1,225
Total	7,529	9,641	9,011	9,223	9,426	10,615	11,264	11,165

[1] Domestic production plus imports, minus exports, and minus estimated utilization for food, industry and other non-feed uses.
Source: *Soybean Blue Book*, 1951, p. 48.
[2] Forecast on basis of October 1950 indications.
[3] Dried and concentrated skim milk, buttermilk, and whey manufactured for animal food.
[4] Dry equivalent of skim milk, buttermilk, whey, and whole milk estimated fed on farms.

TABLE 15. Relationships between the Prices of Soybean Meal and Prices of Other High-Protein Feeds[1]

Feed	Period Covered[2]	Values in Regression Equation[3] a	b	Coefficient of Determination[4]
Cottonseed meal, 41 per cent, Memphis	1930–1949	−3.77	.925	.967
Linseed meal, 36 per cent, Minneapolis	1930–1949	7.84	.818	.945
Peanut meal, 45 per cent, Southeastern milling points	1930–1949	−1.50	.902	.981
Tankage, 60 per cent, Chicago	1930–1949	2.93	1.39	.900
Meat scraps, Chicago	1935–1949	15.08	1.15	.927
Fish meal, 67 per cent, San Francisco	1935–1949	−26.84	2.40	.888
Gluten feed, 23 per cent, Chicago	1930–1949	−1.57	.772	.976
Brewers' dried grains, Milwaukee	1933–1949	−1.38	.724	.980
Distillers' dried grains, Cincinnati	1935–1949	2.05	.845	.992

[1] Source: *The Feed Situation,* January–February 1951 (B.A.E., U.S. Department of Agriculture), p. 20.

The results shown are based on a simple correlation between the calendar-year average prices of soybean meal at Chicago and prices of the various feeds at the specified markets.

[2] The years 1943–1946, when maximum price regulations were in effect, were excluded from the analysis.

[3] Values in regression equation $X_1 = a + bX_2$:

X_1 = price of specified feed, and X_2 = price of soybean meal.

Example: Price of cottonseed meal $= -3.77 + (.925 \times 77.20) = 67.64$.

[4] Coefficient of correlation squared. The coefficients indicate the closeness of the association between soybean meal prices and prices of the other feeds. A coefficient of 1.00 indicates perfect correlation, while 0 indicates no correlation. The coefficients of determination, computed on the basis of the association of the *year-to-year changes* in the prices of soybean meal and the other high-protein feeds, follow. Soybean meal as associated with: cottonseed meal .80; linseed meal .58; peanut meal .86; gluten feed .79; distillers' dried grains .94; brewers' dried grains .86; tankage .42; meat scraps .07; fish meal .12.

TABLE 16. Soybean Oil, Crude Basis: Production, Trade, Stocks December 31, and Apparent Disappearance, 1910–September 1950, by Number of Thousand Pounds[1]

Year	Factory Production	Imports[2]	Exports	Re-exports	Net Imports or (−) Net Exports	Factory and Warehouse Stocks Dec. 31	Apparent Disappearance
1910	Unavailable	20,152	Unavailable	...		Unavailable	
1911	Unavailable	32,242	Unavailable	...		Unavailable	
1912	Unavailable	24,959	Unavailable	184		Unavailable	
1913	Unavailable	14,221	Unavailable	36		Unavailable	
1914	Unavailable	12,555	Unavailable	3		Unavailable	
1915	Unavailable	21,335	Unavailable	76		Unavailable	
1916	Unavailable	145,409	Unavailable	2,063		Unavailable	
1917	Unavailable	264,926	Unavailable	3,977		Unavailable	
1918	Unavailable	335,984	Unavailable	545		Unavailable	
1919	Unavailable	195,808	27,715[3]	17,833		68,830	
1920	Unavailable	112,214	43,512	3,228	65,474	31,243	103,061
1921	Unavailable	17,283	1,944	511	14,828	11,141	34,061
1922	751	17,294	2,458	419	14,417	5,480	20,829
1923	1,404	41,679	1,356	172	40,151	9,451	37,584
1924	950	9,125	2,264	277	6,584	2,836	14,149
1925	2,520	19,493	520	1,748	17,225	2,458	20,123
1926	2,646	30,712	1,567	545	28,600	7,723	25,981
1927	3,088	14,915	5,444	1,184	8,287	6,291	12,807
1928	4,716	13,116	7,142	852	5,122	6,073	10,056
1929	11,009	19,489	7,967	129	11,393	15,631	12,844
1930	14,387	8,348	4,962	517	2,869	15,178	17,709
1931	39,150	4,916	4,551	898	−533	18,650	35,145
1932	39,445	405	2,647	46	−2,288	16,552	39,255

TABLE 16. *Continued*

Year	Factory Production	Imports [2]	Exports	Re-exports	Net Imports or (—) Net Exports	Factory and Warehouse Stocks Dec. 31	Apparent Disappearance
1933	26,533	3,669	1,569	...	2,100	13,534	31,651
1934	35,366	2,829	2,040	...	789	19,007	30,682
1935	105,056	14,249	4,111	...	10,138	31,090	103,111
1936	225,297	4,217 [4]	3,954	...	263	34,416	222,234
1937	194,411	22,259 [4]	5,748	...	16,511	62,317	183,021
1938	323,343	2,856 [4]	6,412	...	—3,556	76,709	305,395
1939	457,550	4,126	12,111	...	—7,985	71,562	454,712
1940	533,224	4,849	15,954	...	—11,105	94,555	499,126
1941	585,629	759	12,066	...	—11,307	113,020	555,857
1942	761,582	...	19,428	...	—19,428	144,139	711,035
1943	1,233,751	... [5]	57,351	...	—57,351	186,566	1,133,973
1944	1,245,873	...	79,513	...	—79,513	123,323	1,229,603
1945	1,391,650	... [5]	40,463	...	—40,463	209,347	1,265,163
1946	1,454,339	...	90,444	...	—90,444	163,937	1,409,305
1947	1,542,984	71	109,760	...	—109,689	146,208	1,451,024
1948	1,604,320	365	85,669	...	—85,304	193,199	1,472,025
1949	1,859,066	239	372,082	...	—371,843	153,930	1,526,492
1950	1,430,591	... [5]	215,865	...	—215,865	117,311 [6]	1,251,345

[1] Source: *Soybean Blue Book*, 1951, p. 49.
[2] Imports for consumption 1910, 1911, and beginning January 1934.
[3] July–December. Not separately reported before July 1919.
[4] Excludes "special imports" entered free of duty for subsequent export.
[5] Less than 500 pounds.
[6] September 30.

TABLE 17. State-to-State Movement of Soybean Oil, 1950[1]

	Number of Cars	Percentage of Total Cars
Illinois to:		
California	3	2.4
Connecticut	1	0.8
Florida	1	0.8
Georgia	4	3.2
Illinois	18	14.3
Kansas	2	1.6
Kentucky	6	4.8
Louisiana	10	7.9
Maine	1	0.8
Michigan	1	0.8
New Jersey	17	13.5
New York	15	11.9
Ohio	8	6.3
Pennsylvania	2	1.6
Tennessee	29	23.0
Texas	3	2.4
Virginia	4	3.2
Wisconsin	1	.8
Total in sample	126	100.1
Indiana to:		
Georgia	2	8.3
Kentucky	1	4.2
New Jersey	13	54.2
New York	2	8.3
Ohio	6	25.0
Total in sample	24	100.0
Minnesota to:		
California	1	8.3
Minnesota	6	50.0[2]
New Jersey	2	16.7
Ohio	1	8.3
Texas	1	8.3
Wisconsin	1	8.3
Total in sample	12	99.9
Iowa to:		
California	1	2.3
Illinois	3	7.0
Louisiana	1	2.3
Minnesota	1	2.3
New Jersey	12	27.9
New York	4	9.3
Ohio	3	7.0
Tennessee	5	11.6
Texas	9	20.9
Wisconsin	4	9.3
Total in sample	43	99.9
Missouri to:		
Kentucky	1	10.0
Ohio	1	10.0
Tennessee	4	40.0
Texas	4	40.0
Total in sample	10	100.0
Ohio to:		
Connecticut	1	2.9
Georgia	1	2.9
Illinois	1	2.9
Louisiana	1	2.9
New Jersey	20	57.1
New York	7	20.0
Ohio	2	5.7
Pennsylvania	2	5.7
Total in sample	35	100.1

[1] Source: Interstate Commerce Commission, Carload Waybill Analyses, 1950, *State-to-State Movement of Manufacturers and Miscellaneous Goods.*

[2] The figure 50 per cent for soybean oil shipments originating and terminating in Minnesota seems to be incorrect and is probably due to the small sample obtained.

TABLE 18. Vegetable Oils: Wholesale Prices, in Cents per Pound, at Specified Markets, Annual Averages, 1930 through 1950[1]

Year	Cottonseed Oil, Crude, Tanks, Southeastern Mills	Linseed Oil, Raw, Tank Cars, Minneapolis	Soybean Oil, Tank Cars, Midwestern Mills
1930	6.9	11.8	8.6
1931	5.3	7.8	5.5
1932	3.1	5.7	3.1
1933	3.7	8.5	5.4
1934	5.6	9.0	6.0
1935	9.2	8.8	8.1
1936	8.6	9.5	7.5
1937	8.0	10.3	8.1[2]
1938	6.7	8.7	5.6
1939	5.6	8.8	4.8
1940	5.3	9.0	4.7
1941	9.5	9.7	8.5
1942	12.7	12.3	11.6
1943	12.8	14.4	11.8
1944	12.8	14.3	11.8
1945	12.8	14.3	11.8
1946	15.8	18.4	14.6
1947	25.9	34.0	23.3
1948	25.3	27.8	22.3
1949	11.6	22.7	11.0
1950	15.7	16.5	14.1

[1] Source: "Cottonseed Oil and Other Food Fats and Oils: Supply and Competitive Relationships," unpublished report and graphs supplied by R. Foote, B.A.E., U.S. Department of Agriculture.

[2] Average for less than 12 months.

TABLE 19. Wholesale Prices, in Cents per Pound, of Leading Fats and Oils, United States, for Specified Periods[1]

Item	Average 1937–1941	November 1949	1950 September	1950 October	1950 November
Butter, 92-score, Chicago	29.6	62.0	62.7	63.2	64.0
Lard, tank car lots, Chicago	7.7	9.2	14.0	12.5	13.7
Cottonseed oil, crude, southeastern mills	7.0	9.6	17.9	18.5	20.6
Soybean oil, crude, midwestern mills	6.4	9.6	15.0	14.6	17.1
Tallow, inedible, prime, Chicago	6.3	5.9	12.3	12.5	13.4
Coconut oil, crude, tank cars, Pacific Coast[2]	7.0	16.7	20.2	18.9	20.1
Linseed oil, raw, tank cars, Minneapolis	9.3	16.7	17.0	15.2	15.4
Tung oil, drums, New York	21.7	27.2	26.5	25.8	26.4

[1] Source: *The Fats and Oils Situation,* November 1950 (B.A.E., U.S. Department of Agriculture), p. 7.

Wholesale prices compiled from *Oil, Paint, and Drug Reporter,* the *National Provisioner,* and reports of the Production and Marketing Administration.

[2] Three cents added to allow for tax on first domestic processing.

TABLE 20. State-to-State Movements of Soybeans

	Number of Cars			Percentage of Total Cars		
	1948	1949	1950	1948	1949	1950
Illinois to:						
California	...	1	...	....	0.2	....
Illinois	292	399	341	86.9	87.7	88.8
Indiana	26	16	14	7.7	3.5	3.6
Iowa	2	12	14	0.6	2.6	3.6
Kansas	...	...	1	....	....	0.3
Kentucky	1	1	5	0.3	0.2	1.3
Louisiana	...	3	...	....	0.7	....
Maryland	...	10	...	....	2.2	....
Minnesota	1	...	...	0.3	....	....
Missouri	4	5	4	1.2	1.1	1.0
New Jersey	2	...	...	0.6	....	....
New York	1	...	...	0.3	....	....
Ohio	6	5	4	1.8	1.1	1.0
Pennsylvania	...	1	...	....	0.2	....
Tennessee	1	1	...	0.3	0.2	....
Virginia	...	1	...	....	0.2	....
Wisconsin	...	...	1	....	....	0.3
Total in sample	336	455	384	100.0	99.9	99.9
Indiana to:						
Illinois	30	40	20	19.5	20.5	15.3
Indiana	58	77	59	37.7	39.5	45.0
Kentucky	9	13	16	5.8	6.7	12.2
Maryland	...	6	...	....	3.1	....
Ohio	57	57	35	37.0	29.2	26.7
Pennsylvania	...	...	1	....	....	0.8
Virginia	...	2	...	....	1.0	....
Total in sample	154	195	131	100.0	100.0	100.0
Iowa to:						
California	1	...	1	0.6	....	0.8
Illinois	14	20	10	8.6	11.3	8.5
Indiana	...	2	...	....	1.1	....
Iowa	135	125	96	83.3	70.6	81.4
Kansas	2	5	3	1.2	2.8	2.5
Maryland	...	3	...	....	1.7	....
Missouri	5	8	2	3.1	4.5	1.7
Nebraska	2	7	5	1.2	4.0	4.2
Oklahoma	2	...	...	1.2	....	....
Pennsylvania	...	4	...	....	2.3	....
South Dakota	...	2	1	....	1.1	0.8
Wisconsin	1	...	...	0.6	....	....
Virginia	...	1	...	....	0.6	....
Total in sample	162	177	118	99.8	100.0	99.9

TABLE 20. *Continued*

	Number of Cars			Percentage of Total Cars		
	1948	1949	1950	1948	1949	1950
Minnesota to:						
California	4	1	..	4.9	0.9	....
Illinois	12	5	..	14.8	4.5	....
Indiana	1	...	..	1.2	....	....
Iowa	19	36	16	23.5	32.4	25.0
Kansas	..	1	..	....	0.9	....
Louisiana	..	1	..	....	0.9	....
Maryland	..	2	..	....	1.8	....
Minnesota	29	43	44	35.8	38.7	68.8
Missouri	6	4	..	7.4	3.6	....
Nebraska	2	4	..	2.5	3.6	....
North Dakota	..	2	..	....	1.8	....
South Dakota	5	5	..	6.2	4.5	....
Wisconsin	3	7	4	3.7	6.3	6.2
Total in sample	81	111	64	100.0	99.9	100.0
Missouri to:						
Arkansas	3	1	..	4.8	1.5	....
California	..	..	3	....	....	3.2
Illinois	20	9	26	32.3	13.4	27.4
Indiana	..	1	..	....	1.5	....
Iowa	4	4	15	6.5	6.0	15.8
Kansas	6	8	3	9.7	11.9	3.2
Kentucky	..	..	1	....	....	1.1
Louisiana	5	19	15	8.1	28.4	15.8
Missouri	13	24	23	21.0	35.8	24.2
Nebraska	..	1	1	....	1.5	1.1
Oklahoma	4	..	3	6.5	....	3.2
Tennessee	5	..	2	8.1	....	2.1
Texas	2	..	3	3.2	....	3.2
Total in sample	62	67	95	100.2	100.0	100.3
Ohio to:						
Illinois	1	1	..	0.9	0.7	....
Indiana	2	4	4	1.9	2.8	4.9
Maryland	1	18	1	0.9	12.7	1.2
Michigan	...	1	..	....	0.7	....
New Jersey	3	...	..	2.8	....	....
New York	10	8	6	9.3	5.6	7.4
Ohio	88	104	69	82.2	73.2	85.2
Pennsylvania	...	1	..	....	0.7	....
Tennessee	...	...	1	....	....	1.2
Virginia	2	5	..	1.9	3.5	....
Total in sample	107	142	81	99.9	99.9	99.9

TABLE 21. The Cost of the Component Parts of a 300-Ton Capacity, Solvent Extraction-Plant [1]

	Probable Cost in Place
Equipment and installation	
1. Conveyor, bean storage to bean cleaner	$2,300
2. Bean cleaner, including cyclone	4,700
3. Conveyor or spout to day-run bin	600
4. Day-run bin	2,500
5. Conveyor, from day-run bin to surge bin above scale	2,000
6. Magnetic separator	300
7. Surge bin	900
8. Scale, automatic with feeder	1,200
9. Cracking rolls (two)	20,000
10. Conveyor or spout from cracking rolls to bean heater	2,900
11. Bean heater and conditioner	25,000
12. Conveyor, bean heater to flaking rolls	5,000
13. Conveyor, cracked bean runs-around	5,200
14. Cracked bean run-around bin	900
15. Conveyor, from cracked-bean run-around bin to item 12 ahead of flaking rolls	2,500
16. Flaking rolls	70,000
17. Aspiration system, for flaking rolls, including cyclone	2,100
18. Conveyor run around "Redler," from flaking rolls to extractor	20,000
19. Flakes run-around bin	900
20. Magnetic protection, ahead of extractor	300
21. Extractor, including feed hopper	78,000
22. Redler or elevator and conveyor, from extractor to top of desolvetizing equipment	11,000
23. Desolvetizing and toasting equipment	90,000
24. Conveyor and/or elevator, from bottom of toaster to meal cooler	2,000
25. Meal cooler	42,000
26. Conveyor, meal cooler to meal bin	5,300
27. Meal bin	3,300
28. Meal screens	5,000
29. Meal grinding	10,000
30. Aspiration, for grinding, including cyclone	3,100
31. Conveyor, to finished meal storage, or to sacking, or to bulk loading	2,500
32. Surge bin, for sacker	1,600
33. Sacking scale and sacker	4,600
34. Stitcher	2,100
35. Bag conveyor	2,500
36. Surge bin, for bulk loader	1,600

TABLE 21. *Continued*

		Probable Cost in Place
37. Bulk loading scale		$2,400
38. Bulk loader		800
39. Solvent unloading		2,700
40. Solvent storage		4,200
41. Solvent pumps, from unload to storage, and from storage to extractor		1,000
42. Solvent and oil recovery system		65,000
43. Solvent trap (or split tank)		800
44. Oil pump, to oil storage		1,000
45. Oil storage tanks		10,800
46. Oil loading facilities		1,000
47. Oil pump, from tanks to cars		1,200
48. Oil cooler, between items 44 and 45		1,000
49. Oil day tank		800
50. Process piping, material only		13,300
51. Process water tank or safety water tank		2,100
52. Installation of furnished equipment, items 8, 9, 11, 16, 21–25, 41, 42, 44, 48, 49		29,800
53. Start, of supervision		2,000
Buildings and services		
1. Well, plus piping		3,000
2. Well pump, plus surge tank		1,500
3. Power lines, to control panel		1,500
4. Electrical control house		2,500
5. Electrical control panel		3,000
6. Connections to sewers		2,000
7. Water supply tank, plus foundations		6,000
8. Process water cooling tank or tower		4,000
9. Boilers, including stack		53,400
10. Boiler house, plus foundation		23,000
11. Fuel storage		2,500
12. Conveyor or pipe line, from fuel storage to boiler house		2,000
13. Fuel unloading		1,000
14. Outside lines — steam, water, electric power, air		2,000
15. Overhead supports for bean conveyor		3,300
16. Day-bin foundation		2,000
17. Piling, if necessary		....
18. Excavation		2,000
19. Foundations (no piles)		7,000
20. Preparation building	one building separated by fire walls	12,000
21. Extraction building		18,000
22. Meal sacking and storage building		12,000

TABLE 21. *Continued*

	Probable Cost in Place
23. R.R. trackage	$7,000
24. Roadways	2,000
25. Sidewalks and paving	1,000
26. Overhead supports for conveyors between buildings	3,300
27. Loading docks	1,500
28. Piping	50,000
29. Wiring, power and light	17,000
30. Lighting	4,000
31. Insulating	20,000
32. Painting	4,700
33. Heating	4,800
34. Ventilating	1,000
35. Plumbing	700
36. Sprinkling	40,000
37. Cleaning up	2,000
38. Starter and controls	5,000
39. Duct work	1,000
40. Spouting	2,000
41. Ladders, stairs, catwalks, grating, and supports	6,000
42. Instrument installation	600
43. Freight on equipment	5,000
Total	$916,100

[1] Analysis made with the help of George L. Levin, professional engineer.

Guarantees

Oil content of flakes	0.5 to 0.7 per cent
Moisture and volatile content of oil	0.2 per cent
Solvent loss	0.5 to 0.7 per cent of weight of beans
Steam consumption	1,250 lbs. per ton
Water consumption	2,000 gals. per ton at 60° F.
Power consumption	17.5 KWH per ton

TABLE 22. The Price per Ton of Shipping Soybean Meal from Decatur, Illinois, December 1951 [1]

Eastern Territory	Price per Ton	Southern Territory	Price per Ton	Western Territory	Price per Ton
Connecticut, New Briton	$13.08	Alabama, Jackson	$11.54	Iowa, Des Moines	$ 7.00
Delaware, Wilmington	12.26	Arizona, Phoenix	24.51	Kansas, Hutchings	10.92
Illinois, Chicago	5.67	Arkansas, Little Rock	10.71	Minnesota, Mankato	9.38
Indiana, Indianapolis	4.94	California, Hollywood	24.51	Minnesota, Minneapolis	9.06
Maine, Bangar	13.08	California, San Francisco	24.51	Minnesota, St. Cloud	10.92
Maryland, Baltimore	12.05	Colorado, Denver	16.48	Missouri, St. Louis	4.74
Massachusetts, Boston	13.08	Florida, Fort Meyers	15.66	Missouri, Monett	8.86
Michigan, Detroit	6.59	Florida, Palatka	17.51	Montana, Deer Lodge	24.31
New Hampshire, Concord	13.08	Georgia, Augusta	12.77	Nebraska, Grand Island	11.83
New Jersey, Jersey City	12.67	Kentucky, Arlington	6.18	Nebraska, Gurley	14.83
New York, New York	13.08	Louisiana, Baton Rouge	12.57	Nevada, Palisade	24.51
New York, Buffalo	10.61	Mississippi, Gulfport	12.15	New Mexico, Santa Fe	19.16
Ohio, Cleveland	7.21	North Carolina, Charlotteville	12.77	New Mexico, Alaguna	24.51
Pennsylvania, Pittsburgh	10.61	South Carolina, Charleston	13.80	North Dakota, Bismarck	15.24
Pennsylvania, Philadelphia	12.05	Tennessee, Chattanooga	9.89	North Dakota, Fargo	13.32
Rhode Island, Providence	13.08	Idaho, Idaho Falls	24.51	Oklahoma, Blackwell	12.57
Vermont, Burlington	13.08			Oregon, Portland	24.51
Virginia, Norfolk	12.05			South Dakota, Aberdeen	12.57
Virginia, Bridgewater	9.68			Texas, Austin	16.48
West Virginia, Bluefield	12.05			Utah, Ogden	19.98
West Virginia, St. Albans	9.06			Washington, Seattle	24.51
				Wisconsin, Milwaukee	6.59
				Wisconsin, LaCrosse	7.42
				Wyoming, Sheridan	19.78

[1] Source: Milwaukee Railroad.

TABLE 23. The Average Per-Ton Railroad Freight Revenue for Soybeans, Soybean Meal, Cottonseed, Cottonseed Meal, Linseed Meal, and Flax, United States, 1947 through 1950 [1]

	Average Tons per Car	Cost per Ton			Average Tons per Car	Cost per Ton	
	1947				1948		
Soybeans	49.87	$3.17	Originated	Soybeans	50.69	$3.78	Originated
Soybean meal	36.79	4.05	Terminated	Soybean meal	37.60	4.69	Terminated
Cottonseed	30.39	3.49	Originated	Cottonseed	30.76	4.04	Originated
Cottonseed meal	34.34	5.09	Terminated	Cottonseed meal	34.71	5.94	Terminated
Linseed meal	33.45	4.83	Originated	Linseed meal	33.67	5.60	Originated
Flax	46.89	4.75	Terminated	Flax	48.17	5.75	Terminated
	1949				1950		
Soybeans	51.33	$4.21	Originated	Soybeans	50.98	$4.14	Originated
Soybean meal	36.86	5.48	Terminated	Soybean meal	36.14	5.14	Terminated
Cottonseed	31.13	4.74	Originated	Cottonseed	28.36	4.94	Terminated
Cottonseed meal	34.65	6.67	Terminated	Cottonseed meal	33.67	6.17	Terminated
Linseed meal	29.83	5.93	Terminated	Linseed meal	31.00	5.33	Terminated
Flax	48.04	5.94	Terminated	Flax	48.64	6.06	Terminated

[1] Source: Interstate Commerce Commission.

TABLE 24. The Total Freight Traffic, by Number of Cars, for 1947 (Including Duplications)[1]

Area	Soybeans (114,523 Cars)		Soybean Meal (152,660 Cars)		Cottonseed (19,893 Cars)		Cottonseed Meal (49,891 Cars)		Linseed Meal (30,654 Cars)		Flax (22,835 Cars)	
	Originated	Terminated	Originated	Terminated	Originated	Terminated	Originated	Terminated	Originated	Terminated	Originated	Terminated
New England	2	4	20	2,654	1	3	16	521	9	396	0	2
Great Lakes	20,862	22,454	20,829	17,980	2	10	80	891	2,210	2,909	245	238
Central Eastern	17,629	17,426	12,421	15,201	1	6	23	1,256	1,208	1,819	69	359
Eastern District ...	38,493	39,884	33,270	35,835	4	19	119	2,668	3,427	5,124	314	599
Pocahontas	1,037	864	599	1,707	6	6	5	215	230	300	2	10
Southern Region ..	16,978	19,729	18,860	11,385	5,802	5,635	11,979	7,084	2,201	2,104	56	71
Southern District ..	18,015	20,613	19,459	13,092	5,808	5,641	11,984	7,299	2,431	2,404	58	81
Northwestern Region	15,320	12,258	13,738	15,326	11	43	34	814	6,811	4,830	15,767	15,706
Central Western ...	11,234	10,327	10,545	14,705	1,603	1,251	3,635	8,408	3,974	4,442	1,736	1,950
South Western	4,885	4,105	6,522	6,288	6,554	6,761	10,666	7,769	1,029	679	556	351
Western District ...	31,439	26,690	30,805	36,319	8,168	8,055	14,335	16,991	11,814	9,951	18,059	18,007

[1] Source: Interstate Commerce Commission.

TABLE 25. The Total Freight Traffic, by Number of Cars, for 1950 (Including Duplications)[1]

Area	Soybeans (139,918 Cars)		Soybean Meal (186,883 Cars)		Cottonseed (12,492 Cars)		Cottonseed Meal (63,589 Cars)		Linseed Meal (42,027 Cars)		Flax (33,542 Cars)	
	Originated	Terminated	Originated	Terminated	Originated	Terminated	Originated	Terminated	Originated	Terminated	Originated	Terminated
New England	0	4	21	3,772	0	2	16	778	47	896	0	0
Great Lakes	25,118	26,900	29,836	20,248	4	14	45	1,376	3,641	3,267	960	1,732
Central Eastern	19,716	19,813	16,495	20,030	2	6	48	1,848	1,436	2,246	84	631
Eastern District	44,834	46,717	46,352	44,050	6	22	109	4,002	5,124	6,409	1,004	2,363
Pocahontas	1,813	1,299	905	2,329	14	1	3	344	392	370	1	5
Southern Region	22,241	24,213	20,463	13,802	3,065	2,880	11,854	7,151	1,858	2,395	108	284
Southern District	24,054	25,512	21,368	16,131	3,079	2,881	11,857	7,495	2,250	2,765	109	289
Northwestern Region ..	12,442	12,267	16,346	17,174	0	5	67	1,722	11,971	9,904	23,901	23,310
Central Western	14,262	13,316	14,184	20,416	1,173	972	7,514	10,946	4,308	5,359	2,115	2,231
South Western	9,730	7,406	5,365	7,931	3,970	4,842	14,392	11,259	777	819	503	821
Western District	36,434	32,989	35,895	45,521	5,143	5,819	21,973	23,527	17,056	16,082	26,519	26,362

[1] Source: Interstate Commerce Commission.

TABLE 26. Soybeans: Stocks in Various Positions, United States, Quarterly Dates, 1942–1951, by Number of Thousand Bushels[1]

Date	On Farms	Interior Mills, Elevators, and Warehouses	Processing Plants	Terminals	Steel and Wooden Bins	Total
1942						
Oct. 1	3,100	928	1,120	861	.....	6,009
1943						
Jan. 1	88,246	29,505	34,938	3,519	13,500	169,708
Apr. 1	54,399	17,094	28,675	3,187	13,000	116,355
July 1	13,733	5,085	17,246	2,864	8,447	47,375
Oct. 1	4,555	668	4,763	732	1,819	12,537
1944						
Jan. 1	56,211	36,276	44,650	23,719	4,951	165,807
Apr. 1	39,080	17,317	35,203	12,790	4,174	108,564
July 1	10,606	4,970	23,712	4,682	3,824	47,794
Oct. 1	4,612	1,128	5,214	1,323	1,876	14,153
1945						
Jan. 1	42,330	40,137	47,708	24,446	3,523	158,144
Apr. 1	27,773	30,012	32,606	16,508	2,762	109,661
July 1	7,598	6,031	26,387	5,401	957	46,374
Oct. 1	2,928	447	3,548	815	...	7,738
1946						
Jan. 1	43,267	39,572	46,255	24,423	400	153,917
Apr. 1	29,872	18,087	37,299	12,666	25	97,949
July 1	6,802	3,526	23,356	3,424	..	37,108
Oct. 1	2,118	268	1,783	157	..	4,326

TABLE 26. *Continued*

Date	On Farms	Interior Mills, Elevators, and Warehouses	Processing Plants	Terminals	Steel and Wooden Bins	Total
1947						
Jan. 1	37,374	36,145	59,610	21,704	..	154,833
Apr. 1	25,475	19,633	41,744	13,689	..	100,541
July 1	6,389	3,389	28,004	2,258	..	40,040
Oct. 1	2,236	244	2,813	68	..	5,361
1948						
Jan. 1	51,679	28,080	48,900	13,294	..	141,953
Apr. 1	33,110	10,845	36,894	7,613	..	88,462
July 1	4,311	3,238	22,986	1,244	..	31,779
Oct. 1	1,838	128	468	130	..	2,564
1949						
Jan. 1	75,504	36,805	53,416	14,804	..	180,529
Apr. 1	52,279	19,262	36,305	7,206	..	115,052
July 1	9,505	9,134	18,333	3,294	..	40,266
Oct. 1	2,147	213	285	462	..	3,107
1950						
Jan. 1	60,853	34,906	66,508	16,133	..	178,400
Apr. 1	45,778	17,412	47,991	10,241	..	121,422
July 1	7,064	4,329	28,478	6,190	..	46,061
Oct. 1	1,204	242	502	920	..	2,868
1951						
Jan. 1	97,671	38,688	77,163	13,915	..	227,437
Apr. 1	46,114	20,148	62,798	12,513	..	141,573

[1] Source: B.A.E., U.S. Department of Agriculture.

TABLE 27. The Typical Cost to Farmers, in Cents per Bushel, for Soybean Storage on Farms and at Country Elevators, for Three-Month and Six-Month Storage Periods, Midwestern Soybean-Producing States[1]

	Three-Month Storage				Six-Month Storage			
	On Farms, by Type and Initial Cost of Storage Building				On Farms, by Type and Initial Cost of Storage Building			
Cost Elements	A $0.40	B $0.60	C $0.90	At Country Elevators	A $0.40	B $0.60	C $0.90	At Country Elevators
Fixed costs								
Storage space								
Depreciation and interest	2.1	3.2	4.0	..	2.1	3.2	4.0	..
Insurance	0.09	0.3	0.5	..	0.09	0.3	0.5	..
Property taxes	0.04	0.06	0.1	..	0.04	0.06	0.1	..
Total	2.2	3.6	4.6	4.5	2.2	3.6	4.6	9.0
In-and-out handling	1.3	1.3	1.3	..	1.3	1.3	1.3	..
Total	3.5	4.9	5.9	4.5	3.5	4.9	5.9	9.0
Variable costs								
Shrinkage	1.5	1.5	1.5	..	1.5	1.5	1.5	..
Interest on value	2.5	2.5	2.5	2.0	4.1	4.1	4.1	3.6
Insurance on risk	0.3	0.4	0.4	..	0.5	0.7	0.7	..
Property taxes (on soybeans)	..	..	..	..	..	..	..	..
Total	4.3	4.4	4.4	2.0	6.1	6.3	6.3	3.6
Total storage cost	7.8	9.3	10.3	6.5	9.6	11.2	12.2	12.6
Prime cost	5.6	5.7	5.7	6.5	7.4	7.6	7.6	12.6

[1] Ohio, Indiana, Illinois, Missouri, Iowa, Minnesota. These states account for about 90 per cent of the soybeans harvested.

Source: Rollefson, Agnew, Keirstead, *Improving Marketing through Farm Storage* (P.M.A., U.S. Department of Agriculture, June 1951), p. 17.

TABLE 28. Official United States Grades and Grade Requirements for All Classes of Soybeans [1]

Grade [2]	Minimum Test Weight, Pounds per Bushel	Percentage Maximum Limits of			
		Moisture	Splits	Damaged Kernels (Soybean and Other Grains)	Foreign Material
No. 1	56	13.0	10.0	2.0	2.0
No. 2	54	14.0	20.0	3.0	3.0
No. 3	52	16.0	30.0	5.0	4.0
No. 4	49	18.0	40.0	8.0	6.0
Sample grade	Sample grade shall be soybeans which do not meet the requirements for any of the grades from No. 1 to No. 4, inclusive; or which are musty or sour, or heating; or which have any commercially objectionable foreign odor; or which contain stones; or which are otherwise of distinctly low quality.				

[1] Source: U.S. Department of Agriculture, *Handbook of Official Grain Standards of the United States, 1950,* p. 72.

[2] The soybeans in grade No. 1 of the class Yellow Soybeans may contain not more than 1.0 per cent, in grade No. 2 not more than 2.0 per cent, and in grade No. 3 not more than 5.0 per cent of Green, Black, Brown, or bicolored soybeans, either singly or in any combination.

Soybeans which are materially weathered shall not be graded higher than No. 4.

Discounts

Test weight: ½ cent per bushel for each pound or fraction thereof under 54 lbs.

Moisture: 1½ cents per bushel for each 0.5 per cent moisture in excess of 14 per cent.

Splits: ¼ cent per bushel for each 5 per cent or fraction thereof in excess of 20 per cent.

Green damage: 2/10 of 1 cent per bushel for each 1 per cent or fraction thereof in excess of 3 per cent total damage.

Foreign material: All foreign material in excess of 3 per cent shall be deducted from the gross weight and will not be paid for.

Appendix II. Interviews

APPENDIX II

Interviews

Martin Achkenazy, Oil broker
O. F. Anderson, O.F.A.R., U.S. Department of Agriculture
D. O. Andreas, Cargill, Inc.
Lowell W. Andreas, Honeymead Products Co., Mankato
Louis Bean, Secretary's Office, U.S. Department of Agriculture
E. F. Benson, Archer-Daniels-Midland Co.
Emil Berens, Falk Co.
Wilbur P. Bidne, Farmers Coop. Soybean Plant, Blooming Prairie
J. D. Black, Harvard University
Jay Bolton, Atwood Larson Co.
Milton Bondus, Cargill, Inc.
Walter T. Borg, P.M.A., U.S. Department of Agriculture
Frank V. Caesar, Freight Traffic Service
M. Clough, B.A.E., U.S. Department of Agriculture
John Evans, American Soybean Association
Carl Farrington, Archer-Daniels-Midland Co.
F. M. Ferguson, The Glidden Co.
W. W. Fetrow, F.C.A., U.S. Department of Agriculture
George Fishwick, Merrill Lynch, Pierce, Fenner & Beane
Dean Fisk, Cargill, Inc.
R. J. Foote, B.A.E., U.S. Department of Agriculture
Karl A. Fox, B.A.E., U.S. Department of Agriculture
E. A. Funk, Jr., Funk Brothers Seed Co.
C. B. Gilliland, P.M.A., U.S. Department of Agriculture
J. Giovanna, Decatur Soy Products
J. C. Givens, Engineer, Crown Iron Works
Max Goldberg, Moorhead Seed & Grain Co.
Ralph Golseth, The Glidden Co.
Harold Goodwin, Funk Brothers Seed Co.
Prof. Hackelman, University of Illinois
Fred Haffner, General Mills, Inc.
Miss Alice E. Haggins, Chicago Board of Trade
C. A. Harvey, North Dakota State Mill & Elevator
Jack Haymacker, Cargill, Inc.
J. W. Hayward, Archer-Daniels-Midland Co.
T. A. Heironymus, University of Illinois
Julius Hendel, Cargill, Inc.
J. Hodek, Pittsburgh Plate and Glass Co.
R. G. Houghtlin, National Soybean Processors Ass'n.
Donald Jackson, P.M.A., U.S. Department of Agriculture
R. D. Jennings, B.A.E., U.S. Department of Agriculture
H. J. Kapp, Staley Manufacturing Co.
Ray Keebler, Hallet & Carey
C. H. Keirstead, P.M.A., U.S. Department of Agriculture
Ray King, Cargill, Inc.
David Levin, Continental Grain Co.
George L. Levin, Soybean construction engineer
Sherman Levin, Continental Grain Co.
Riley Lewis, Consumer's Soybean Mills, Inc.
Ray Lindquist, Minnesota Linseed Oil Co.

J. Lynch, Chicago Board of Trade
K. J. Maltas, Staley Manufacturing Co.
Ralph H. Manley, General Mills, Inc.
Clive P. Marshall, Honeymead Products Co.
James Maslon, Honeymead Products Co.
Carl Matzoll, Milwaukee Railroad
Kenneth McCoy, Cargill, Inc.
M. D. McVay, Cargill, Inc.
James Mullin, Leval Grain Co.
L. J. Norton, University of Illinois
Joseph Oberhauser, Milwaukee Road
C. J. Olson, Farmers & Merchants Soybean Co.
Robert Parrot, Cargill, Inc.
L. H. Patton, Oil and meal broker
E. L. Peterson, Traffic Manager, Mpls. Grain Exchange
J. J. Quinlan, Allied Mills, Inc.
K. Quintance, North Dakota State Mill & Elevator
Paul E. Quintus, O.F.A.R., U.S. Department of Agriculture
A. M. Rollefson, P.M.A., U.S. Department of Agriculture
Irving J. Rosen, Quincy Soybean Products Co.
Norman Rosen, Quincy Soybean Products Co.
George W. Sandahl, Spencer Kellogg
Louis Sandbaakken, Plant Manager, Co-op., Dawson
Milton Sandberg, Hallet & Carey
R. Schickele, North Dakota Agricultural College
Bob Schulte, Denco Company
Geoffrey Shephard, Iowa State College
Joseph Sinaiko, Iowa Milling Co.
C. C. Spilsbury, P.M.A., U.S. Department of Agriculture
E. G. Strand, B.A.E., U.S. Department of Agriculture
George Strayer, American Soybean Association
Thomas Totachek, Cargill, Inc.
H. L. Walster, North Dakota Agricultural College
E. F. Wells, Interstate Commerce Commission
Richard Weslie, Cargill, Inc.
Robert White, Archer-Daniels-Midland Co.

Bibliography and Index

Bibliography

BOOKS

Bailey, Alton E. *Cottonseed and Cottonseed Products.* New York: Interscience Publishers Inc., 1951.

Curtis, Robert S. *Cottonseed Meal – Origin, History, Research.* Raleigh, N.C.: Robert S. Curtis Publishing Co., 1938.

Dies, Jerome Edward. *Soybeans, Gold from the Soil.* New York: Macmillan Co., 1942.

Directory and Handbook of the Meat and Provision Trades and Their Allied Industries. New York: National Provisioner Publishing Co., 1895.

Hedlund, E. C. *The Transportation Economics of the Soybean Industry.* University of Illinois Press, 1952.

Horvath, A. A. *The Soybean Industry.* New York: Chemical Publishing Co., 1939.

International Library of Technology. *Packinghouse Industries, Cottonseed Oil and Products, Manufacturer of Leather, Manufacturer of Soap.* Scranton: International Textbook Co., 1902.

Lager, Mildred. *The Useful Soybean.* New York: McGraw-Hill Book Co., Inc., 1945.

Markley, Klare S., ed. *Soybeans and Soybean Products.* 2 vols. New York: Interscience Publishers Inc., 1951.

Mighell, R. L., and J. D. Black. *Interregional Competition in Agriculture.* Cambridge, Mass.: Harvard University Press, 1951.

Piper, Charles V., and William J. Morse. *The Soybean.* New York: McGraw-Hill Book Co., Inc., 1923.

Ramsay, Richard E. *Financing the Soybean Processor.* Graduate School of Banking, Rutgers University, 1950. Privately published.

Wheeler, W. A. *Forage and Pasture Crops.* New York: D. Van Nostrand Co., Inc., 1950.

Unpublished

Hendel, Julius. "Relationship Between the Price of Cash Hard Red Spring Wheat and Futures in the Minneapolis Market." Ph.D. thesis, University of Minnesota, 1928.

Hieronymus, T. A. "The Economics of Risk in the Marketing of Soybeans and Soybean Products." Ph.D. thesis, University of Illinois, 1949.

Jen, Yun Hsiang. "Criteria for Estimating Relative Maturity of Soybean Varieties and the Relationship of Stage of Maturity to Yield and Quality." M.S. thesis, University of Minnesota, 1949.

Kretzschmar, Gerhard P. "A Study of the Insect Population Found on Soybeans in Minnesota during One Season with Special Reference to Sampling Methods." M.S. thesis, University of Minnesota, 1947.

Malitsky, Valentine S. "The Production and Foreign Trade of Soybeans in the United States." M.S. thesis, University of Minnesota, 1931.

Mann, Robert L. "A Study of the Proteins of Soybeans." Ph.D. thesis, University of Minnesota, 1949.

Mehta, Tribhuwan Ram. "Correlation of Yield and Certain Quantitative Characteristics in Soybeans." Ph.D. thesis, University of Minnesota, 1948.

Milner, Max. "The Respiration and Storage Behavior of Soybeans." Ph.D. thesis, University of Minnesota, 1945.

Morrow, Kenneth S. "Soybean Hay as a Feed for Dairy Cows." M.S. thesis, University of Minnesota, 1925.

Olmstead, Robert H. "The Soybean as a Source of Protein in the Dairy Ration." M.S. thesis, University of Minnesota, 1923.

Paul, A. B. "Economic Factors in the Growth of the Oilseed Industry in the United States." Ph.D. thesis, University of Illinois, 1947.

Ramstad, Paul Ellerston. "A Study of the Respiration and Storage Behavior of Soybeans." Ph.D. thesis, University of Minnesota, 1942.

Von Frank, George O. "The Economics of the Soybean Industry." Ph.D. thesis, Columbia University, 1948.

Warren, F. G. "Economic Significance of the Futures Market for Soybeans." Ph.D. thesis, University of Illinois, 1945.

West, V. I. "Evalution of Certain Systems for Differentiating Market Qualities of Soybeans." Ph.D. thesis, University of Illinois, 1951.

PAMPHLETS AND PERIODICALS

Abstracts of talks presented at the Minnesota Soybean Institute March 4 and 5, 1948, Department of Agriculture, Agricultural Short Courses, University of Minnesota, 1948.

Agnew, D. B., and C. H. Keirstead. *Cash Costs of Farm Storage in Marketing Soybeans.* (P.M.A., Fats and Oils Branch, U.S. Department of Agriculture.) Washington, D.C., September 1950.

Agricultural Price Support Programs for 1951–52 with Futures Market Equivalents and Price Ceilings. Merrill Lynch, Pierce, Fenner & Beane, New York, August 1951.

Akers, Howard A. *Observations on the Vegetable Oils Situation in Certain Countries of Europe and in Source Areas of Africa.* (U.S. Department of Agriculture, Foreign Agriculture Report No. 40.) Washington, D.C., October 1949.

Animal Units of Livestock Fed Annually, 1919–20 to 1948–49. (B.A.E., U.S. Department of Agriculture.) Washington, D.C., October 1949.

Animal Units of Livestock Fed Annually, 1947–48 to 1950–51. (B.A.E., U.S. Department of Agriculture.) Washington, D.C., April 1951.

Annual Report, Duluth Board of Trade, December 31, 1950. Duluth, Minn.

Annual Report of a Study of Crop Production Costs and Returns in South Central Minnesota. Minnesota Valley Canning Co., and Division of Agricultural Economics, University of Minnesota, Le Sueur, Minn., January 1949.

Annual Reports of the Board of Trade of the City of Chicago, 1948–1950.

Annual Reports of the Minneapolis Grain Exchange, 1939–1950.

Annual Review for 1949 of Oilseeds, Oils, Oilcakes, and Other Commodities. Frank Fehr & Company, London, England.

Arthur D. Little, Inc. *Marketing Potential for Oilseed Protein Materials in Industrial Uses.* (U.S. Department of Agriculture, Technical Bulletin, No. 1043.) Washington, D.C., September 1951.

Barnes, R. H., and J. E. Maack. *Review of Literature on Nutritive Value of Soybeans.* University of Minnesota, Minneapolis, 1943.

"Beans High Oil Cheap: Processors in Trouble," *Business Week,* February 4, 1950.

"Blackhawk, New Early Soybean for the Corn Belt, Excels Older Varieties in Yield and Oil Content," *Crops and Soils,* March 1951.

Briggs, G. M., H. J. Sloane, Cora Cooke, and W. A. Billings. *Formula Chart for Poultry Mashes.* (University of Minnesota Agricultural Extension Service.) St. Paul, February 1951.

Carload Waybill Analyses, 1947, 1948, 1949, and 1950, *Territorial Movement, Products of Agriculture.* Interstate Commerce Commission, Washington, D.C., May 1949, October 1949, August 1950, and July 1951.

Carload Waybill Analyses, 1948, 1949, and 1950, *State-to-State Distribution of Products of Agriculture Traffic and Revenue.* Interstate Commerce Commission, Washington, D.C., May 1950, December 1950, and July 1951.

Carload Waybill Analyses, 1950, *Average Revenue Progressions by Specified Mileage Blocks for Commodity Groups and Classes.* Interstate Commerce Commission, Washington, D.C., September 1951.

Carload Waybill Analyses, 1950, *Mileage Distribution of Carloads for Each Commodity Class by Type of Car.* Interstate Commerce Commission, Washington, D.C., November 1951.

Carload Waybill Analyses, 1950, *State-to-State Distribution of Manufacturers and Miscellaneous and Forwarder Traffic.* Interstate Commerce Commission, Washington, D.C., October 1951.

Carload Waybill Analyses, 1951, *Quarterly Comparisons Traffic and Revenue by Commodity Classes,* Terminations in First Quarter 1947–1951. Interstate Commerce Commission, Washington, D.C., September 1951.

Carload Waybill Analyses, 1950. *Weight Distribution of Carloads for Each Commodity Class by Type of Car.* Interstate Commerce Commission, Washington, D.C., November 1951.

Cartter, J. L., and T. H. Hopper. *Influence of Variety, Environment, and Fertility Level on the Chemical Composition of Soybean Seed.* (U.S. Department of Agriculture, Technical Bulletin No. 787.) Washington, D.C., May 1942.

Census of Manufacturers 1947, Grain-Mill Products. (U.S. Department of Commerce.) Washington, D.C., 1949.

"Corn Beats Beans in Cash Return," *Wallace's Farmer,* April 7, 1951.

"Corn or Beans on Last Field?" *Wallace's Farmer,* May 5, 1951.

Cottonseed Oil for Forty-two Years. Merrill Lynch, Pierce, Fenner & Beane, New York, September 1951.

Country Soybean Production in Specified States. Industrial Department, Chicago, Rock Island, and Pacific Railroad Co., Chicago, Ill.

Cox, Rex W. *Minnesota Farmer's Interest in Fats and Oil-Bearing Products.* (Agricultural Experiment Station, University of Minnesota, Bulletin No. 376.) Minneapolis, June 1944.

Cracking the Soybean. Archer-Daniels-Midland Co., Minneapolis, Minn.

Crown Safe-Solvent Process. Crown Iron Works Co., of Minneapolis, Minn.

Crude Soybean Oil Futures. Chicago Board of Trade, October 24, 1950.

Engene, S. A., and G. A. Pond, *Farm Accounting Route in Nicollet County, Minnesota.* (Division of Agricultural Economics, Mimeographed Report No. 158.) St. Paul, Minn.

Estimated Feed Use and Supplies for the 1950–51 Feeding Year. American Feed Manufacturers Ass'n., Chicago 4, Ill.

Facts for Industry, Fats and Oils. (Bureau of the Census, Department of Commerce.) Washington, D.C., Monthly, 1945–1949, and February 28, 1951.

Fats and Oils. *World Production and Trade in 1950.* (U.S. Department of Agriculture, Foreign Agriculture Circular.) Washington, D.C., March 16, 1951.

The Fats and Oils Situation Reports. (B.A.E., U.S. Department of Agriculture.) Washington, D.C. (especially November 1950, August–September 1951, July 1951).

Faure, J. C. A. *Address at the International Association of Seed Crushers Congress, Brighton, England, June 1951.*

The Feed Situation Reports. (B.A.E., U.S. Department of Agriculture.) Washington, D.C. (especially January–February 1951, July 1951).

Feed Statistics. (B.A.E., U.S. Department of Agriculture, Statistical Bulletin No. 85.) Washington, D.C., December 1949 and December 1950.

Fetrow, Ward W., and Jane L. Scearce. *Working Manual for Cooperative Soybean Oil Mill Operators.* (Farm Credit Association, U.S. Department of Agriculture.) Washington, D.C., November 1945.

Fletcher, M. I., "World Soybean Production in 1948," *Scientific Monthly,* February 1950.

Foreign Agricultural Outlook Charts 1952. (Office of Foreign Agricultural Relations, U.S. Department of Agriculture.) Washington, D.C., October 1951.

Foreign Crops and Markets, Vol. 63, No. 5. (U.S. Department of Agriculture.) Washington, D.C., July 30, 1951.

French Oil Continuous Solvent Extraction Systems. The French Oil Mill Machinery Company, Pique, Ohio.

Funk, E. D., Jr. *The Early History of Soybean Contracts with Farmers and Elevators.* Bloomington, Ill., June 7, 1951.

Golseth, Ralph G. *Trading in Fats and Oils.* (Fourth Annual Symposium, Commodity Markets and the Public Interest.) Chicago, September 6, 1951.

Hafner, Fred H. "Soybean Meal Newsletter," *Nutritionews,* General Mills, Inc., December 1951.

Hansen, Peter L., and Ronald L. Nighell. *Oil Crops in American Farming.* (U.S. Department of Agriculture, Technical Bulletin No. 940.) Washington, D.C., November 1947.

Hayes, H. K., E. R. Ausemus, I. O. Culbertson, J. W. Lambert, and R. G. Robinson. *Varietal Trials of Farm Crops.* (Agricultural Experiment Station, University of Minnesota, Miscellaneous Report No. 12.) Minneapolis, February 1951.

———. *Varietal Trials of Farm Crops.* (Agricultural Experiment Station, University of Minnesota, Miscellaneous Report No. 15.) Minneapolis, February 1952.

Hayward, J. W. "Recent Developments in Soybean Oil Meal Processing, Research and Utilization," *Feedstuffs,* July 29, 1950.

———. "Soybean Products as a Feed for Livestock and Poultry," *Feedstuffs,* December 5 and 12, 1942.

———. "Soybean Oil Meal Processing," *Flour and Feed* (Milwaukee, Wis.), September 1940.

———. "The Nutritive Value of Soybean Oil Meal Prepared by the Different Methods of Extraction," *Soap and Oil,* December 1937.

Heller, D. "Rise of the Soybean," *Farm Quarterly,* Autumn 1950.

Hendel, Julius. *Economics of Price Behavior.* Lecture to Cargill Trainee Program, March 17, 1948, Minneapolis, Minn.

———. *Soybeans in the World Fats and Oils Picture.* American Soybean Association Meeting, 1950.

Hughes, P. C. "Raise More Soybeans on Same Acres," *Wallace's Farmer,* April 21, 1951.

Hurst, F. "Co-ops Help in Switch to Soybeans," *News Farmer Crops,* May 1951.

"Improvement and Industrial Utilization of Soybeans," *Research under the Soybean.* Laboratory Program. (U.S. Department of Agriculture, Miscellaneous Publication No. 623.) Washington, D.C., September 1947.

Jackson, Donald. *Storage Situation at Oil Mills.* (Marketing Activities, U.S. Department of Agriculture.) Washington, D.C., October 1951.

Jennings, R. D. *A Look at the Protein Situation for Livestock.* (B.A.E., U.S. Department of Agriculture.) Washington, D.C., March 1950.

———. *The Deficit in Protein for Livestock.* (U.S. Department of Agriculture.) Washington, D.C., April 1946.

Johnson, Hugh A. *The Future of Flax and Soybean Production in Southwestern Minnesota.* (Agricultural Experiment Station, University of Minnesota, and B.A.E. of the U.S. Department of Agriculture.) Milwaukee, Wis., April 1946.

Jordon, G. L. *What Determines Soybean Prices.* (Agricultural Experiment Station, University of Illinois, Bulletin 546.)

Lambert, J. W. "Are Soybeans Here to Stay," *Minnesota Farm and Home Science* (Agricultural Experiment Station, University of Minnesota), Vol. 6, No. 2, February 1949.

The Livestock and Meat Situation Reports. (B.A.E., U.S. Department of Agriculture.) Washington, D.C. (especially October 1951).

Maltas, K. J. *Staley's Soybean Oil Meal.* A. E. Staley Manufacturing Co., Decatur, Ill., 1936.

Maslon, J. I. *Trainee Report Northwest Linseed Division Falk & Co.*, August 9, 1950.

Merrill Lynch, Pierce, Fenner & Beane. Various commodity reports of the Com modity Research Bureau, Inc., New York.

Minnesota Agricultural Statistics, 1949–1950. State-Federal Crop and Livestock Reporting Service, St. Paul, Minn.

Minnesota State Farm Census, 1950. State-Federal Crop and Livestock Reporting Service, St. Paul, Minn.

Morse, W. J., and others. *Soybean Culture and Varieties.* (U.S. Department of Agriculture, Farmers Bulletin No. 1520.) Washington, D.C., 1949.

Nodland, T. R., G. A. Pond, and B. F. Stanton. *Annual Report of the Southeastern Minnesota Farm Management Service.* (Division of Agricultural Economics, University of Minnesota, Mimeographed Report No. 180.) St. Paul, April 1950.

———. *Annual Report of the Southwestern Minnesota Farm Management Service.* (Division of Agricultural Economics, University of Minnesota, Mimeographed Report No. 181.) St. Paul, May 1950.

Norton, L. J. *Export Outlook for United States Fats, Oils, and Oilseed in Selected European Countries.* (U.S. Department of Agriculture, Foreign Agriculture Report No. 44.) Washington, D.C., December 1949.

———. *Report on Fats and Oils Situation in Italy.* (O.F.A.R., U.S. Department of Agriculture, Foreign Agriculture Circular.) Washington, D.C., October 28, 1949.

Official Minnesota Grain Grades. The Minnesota Board of Grain Appeals, Minneapolis, Minn.

Oil Mills Crushing Major Vegetable Oilseeds, 1950. (P.M.A., Fats and Oils Branch, U.S. Department of Agriculture.) Washington, D.C.

Pahigian, Noriar. *Marketing Study of the Oil Content of Soybeans as Related to Production Areas and Climate.* (P.M.A., Fats and Oils Branch, U.S. Department of Agriculture.) Washington, D.C., September 1950.

"Personal Incomes Going Up," *U.S. News and World Report* (Dayton, Ohio), September 7, 1951, p. 22.

Pond, George A. *Soybeans in the Minnesota Cropping System.* Talk at Tri-State Soybean Processors' Conference at Columbia, Mo., March 1 and 2, 1950.

Preliminary 1950 Census of Agriculture for Minnesota, Illinois, Iowa, Indiana,

Ohio, Missouri and Mississippi. (U.S. Department of Agriculture.) Washington, D.C. (released in late months of 1951 and early 1952).

Preliminary Resume of the Study of Toxicity of Soybean Meal. Crown Iron Company, 1951.

Procurement Authorizations and Allotments, Economic Cooperation Administration, Division of Statistics and Reports as of June 30, 1951. Washington, D.C., August 22, 1951.

Production and Distribution of Cottonseed Oil Meals, Soybean Oil Meals, and Linseed Oil Meals by States, January 1944–October 1946. (P.M.A., Grain Branch, U.S. Department of Agriculture.)

Results of the Cooperative Uniform Soybean Tests, 1950. Part I, North Central States, and Part II, Southern States. (U.S. Department of Agriculture.) Washington, D.C., March 1951.

Robinson, C. E. *Hedging Problems of Soybean Processors.* Talk at Soybean Conference at Peoria, Illinois. (Commodity Exchange Authority, U.S. Department of Agriculture.) Washington, D.C., January 16, 1950.

Rollefson, A. M., D. B. Agnew, and C. H. Keirstead. *Improving Soybean Marketing Through Farm Storage.* (P.M.A., U.S. Department of Agriculture.) Washington, D.C., June 1951.

Rossiter, Fred J., Regina H. Bayle, Douglas M. Crawford, Dale E. Farringer, and Helen Francis. *Fats and Oils World Production and Trade.* (U.S. Department of Agriculture, Foreign Agriculture Report No. 11.) Washington, D.C., August 1946.

Rules, By-Laws, Regulations of the Minneapolis Grain Exchange.

Sabin, A. R. *Marketing Channels and Margins for Soybeans and Soybean Products in Illinois, Crop Years 1947, 1948.* (B.A.E., U.S. Department of Agriculture.) Washington, D.C., October 1950.

Schickele, R., and T. W. Schultz. *Competitive Position of Lard in the Market of Animal and Vegetable Fats and Oils.* (Iowa State College of Agriculture, Research Bulletin No. 171.) Ames, Iowa, March 1934.

Shollenberger, J. H., and Warren H. Goss. *Soybeans: Certain Agronomic, Physical, Chemical, Economic, and Industrial Aspects.* (U.S. Department of Agriculture, Northern Regional Research Laboratory.) Peoria, Ill., May 15, 1945 (revised 1947).

The Soybean Blue Books (1947–1951). American Soybean Association, Hudson, Iowa.

The Soybean Digest. Official Publication of the American Soybean Association, Monthly, from 1940 to February 1952, Hudson, Iowa.

Soybean Diseases and Their Control. (U.S. Department of Agriculture, Farmers Bulletin No. 1937.) Washington, D.C., May 1943.

Soybean Meal Rules and Regulations. Board of Trade of the City of Chicago, Chicago, June 26, 1951.

Soybean News, published by the National Soybean Improvement Council, Decatur, Ind.

Soybean Processors the New Improved N.Y.P.E. Crude Soybean Oil Futures "D" Contract Will Just Suit Your Needs. Commodities, Merrill Lynch, Pierce, Fenner & Beane, New York, January 3, 1951.

Soybean Varieties. (B.A.E., U.S. Department of Agriculture.) Washington, D.C., August 1948.

Soybeans and Soybean Products as Food. (U.S. Department of Agriculture, Miscellaneous Publication No. 534.) Washington, D.C., December 1943.

Soybeans in North Dakota and Northwestern Minnesota. North Dakota Mill & Elevator, Grand Forks, N.D.

Spilsbury, C. C. *Distribution of Marketing and Processing Costs of Cottonseed Oil Mills, 1948–49 Compared with 1947–48.* (P.M.A., Fats and Oils Branch, U.S. Department of Agriculture.) Washington, D.C., June 1951.

The Staley Journal. Published monthly by the A. E. Staley Manufacturing Co., Decatur, Ill.

Stocks of Grains and Oilseeds in Off-Farm Positions by States. (B.A.E., U.S. Department of Agriculture.) Washington, D.C., June 1951.

The Story of Soybeans, Soybean Oil, Soybean Meal, Their Uses and Products. Chicago Board of Trade, Chicago, 1951.

Strand, Edwin G. *Soybeans in American Farming.* (B.A.E., U.S. Department of Agriculture, Technical Bulletin No. 966.) Washington, D.C., November 1948.

Task, S. A. "Soybean Mill Blooms on Prairie," *News Farmer Crops,* February 1951.

The Third Annual Tri-State Soybean Conference of Processors and Agronomists from Illinois, Indiana, Ohio, at the University of Illinois, March 21 and 22, 1951.

Third Annual Tri-State Soybean Processors' Conference, Minnesota – Iowa – Missouri. The National Soybean Processors Association and the Agricultural Experiment Stations, Minneapolis and St. Paul, Minn., March 8 and 9, 1951.

Thirty-First Annual Feed Bulletin. (Division of Feed and Fertilizer Control, State of Minnesota Department of Agriculture.) St. Paul, Minn., 1949.

Tons of Revenue Freight Originated and Tons Terminated in Carloads by Classes of Commodities and by Geographic Areas – Class I Steam Railways, Years 1947–1950. Interstate Commerce Commission, Washington, D.C.

Toole, E. H. and V. K. *Relation of Temperature and Seed Moisture to the Viability of Stored Soybean Seed.* (U.S. Department of Agriculture, Circular No. 753.) Washington, D.C., September 1946.

Tri-State Soybean Processors' Conference – Missouri – Iowa – Minnesota, March 1–2, 1950, Cooperating with the University of Missouri College of Agriculture, Columbia, Mo.

Volume of Futures Trading on All Contract Markets Combined. Memphis Merchants Exchange, Memphis, Tenn., July 27, 1951.

Walsh, Robert M. *Fats and Oils in World War II, Production and Price Supporting Programs.* (B.A.E., U.S. Department of Agriculture, War Records Mimeograph No. 6.) Washington, D.C., October 1947.

Weekly Feed Market Review. (P.M.A., Grain Branch, U.S. Department of Agriculture.) Minneapolis, Minn.

Wells, C. F. *United States Tariff Rates on Agriculture Products* (revised). (U.S. Department of Agriculture.) Washington, D.C., May 1951.

"Which Soybean to Plant?" *Wallace's Farmer,* March 17, 1951.

Wilgus, H. S., L. C. Norris, and G. F. Heuser. "Effect of Heat on Nutritive Value of Soybean Oil Meal," *Industrial and Engineering Chemistry,* May 1936.

World Soybean Production Establishes a New Record. (U.S. Department of Agriculture, Foreign Agriculture Circular.) Washington, D.C., December 13, 1948.

World Soybean Production Reaches All-Time High. (U.S. Department of Agriculture, Foreign Agriculture Circular.) Washington, D.C., May 3, 1951.

World Supplies and Requirements of Milk and Edible Fats. (Food and Agriculture Organization of the United Nations.) Washington, D.C., September 1950.

Year Book and Trading Rules, 1950–1951. National Soybean Processors Association, Chicago.

Index